FAST FWD:

THE FULLY RECOVERED MINDSET

MADELINE NIEBANCK

New Degree Press

FAST FWD:

THE FULLY RECOVERED MINDSET

ISBN	978-1-64137-532-0	*Paperback*
	978-1-64137-533-7	*Kindle Ebook*
	978-1-64137-534-4	*Digital Ebook*

To all the therapists and doctors who have helped me along my recovery journey, you are the real heroes of this story.

CONTENTS

CHAPTER 1.   INTRODUCTION   9

PART 1:   **OBSTACLES ARE OPPORTUNITIES**   **15**
CHAPTER 2.   SHIT HAPPENS   17

PART 2:   **NEW PRIORITIES**   **25**
CHAPTER 3.   SHI(F)T HAPPENS   27
CHAPTER 4.   IT'S NOT JUST FOR WRINKLES   33
CHAPTER 5.   A WHOLE NEW WORLD   39
CHAPTER 6.   WHAC-A-MOLE   43
CHAPTER 7.   PAIN IN THE NECK   47
CHAPTER 8.   ADJUSTING TO THE NEW YOU   51
CHAPTER 9.   POSITIVE HEALTH   53
CHAPTER 10. SUGAR-FREE RASPBERRY, PLEASE   57

PART 3:   **POSITIVE VIBES ONLY**   **63**
CHAPTER 11. LIVE YOUR BEST LIFE   65
CHAPTER 12. SHARE YOUR STROKE OF GENIUS   69
CHAPTER 13. A NEW COMPETITIVE ADVANTAGE   75
CHAPTER 14. "FEAR IS A MOTHERFUCKER"   79
CHAPTER 15. TRUST IN THE LORD WITH ALL YOUR
             HEART—PROVERBS 3:5   85
CHAPTER 16. BIG GIRLS DON'T CRY
             (OR AT LEAST THIS ONE DOESN'T)   89
CHAPTER 17. POSITIVITY, AND ALL THAT JAZZ   95

PART 4:   **GOAL SETTING**   **99**

CHAPTER 18.   GOALS, GOALS, AND MORE GOALS!   101

CHAPTER 19.   LOOK MA, TWO HANDS!   105

CHAPTER 20.   NOT JUST A PIPE DREAM   111

CHAPTER 21.   IT'S ONLY ONE STEP, BUT IT'S A BIG ONE   115

CHAPTER 22.   HEEL COMES THE BRIDE   123

PART 5:   **PUSH IT TO THE LIMIT**   **129**

CHAPTER 23.   LONDON CALLING   131

CHAPTER 24.   NOT JUST ANOTHER FAMILY BARBECUE   135

CHAPTER 25.   RUN THE MILE YOU'RE ON   141

CHAPTER 26.   SPOON THEORY   147

CHAPTER 27.   SOMEONE TURN DOWN THE VOLUME   151

CHAPTER 28.   THE HANGOVER PART IV   155

PART 6:   **A TREE GROWS IN BIRMINGHAM**   **159**

CHAPTER 29.   USE IT OR LOSE IT!   161

CHAPTER 30.   KEEP MOVING, THERE'S NOTHING TO SEE HERE   167

CHAPTER 31.   TURNING LEMONS TO LEMONADE   171

CHAPTER 32.   TODAY IS A BEAUTIFUL DAY TO BE ALIVE   175

CHAPTER 33.   BRAIN BUDDIES   179

CHAPTER 34.   NO BETTER TIME THAN THE PRESENT   183

CHAPTER 35.   SURVIVOR SUNDAY   187

CHAPTER 36.   ONWARD!   191

CHAPTER 37.   EPILOGUE   195

STRATEGIES   199

Obstacles are opportunities.

—GREG NANCE

CHAPTER 1

INTRODUCTION

———

It's a blistering hot day on June 24, 2019. On this sweltering Monday, I find myself in the lobby of the Taub Clinic at the University of Alabama at Birmingham, nervously anticipating the start of what I imagine will be a grueling three weeks. A few minutes later, a woman steps out to greet me, and I reach out to shake her hand. Except I can't because she offers me her left hand to shake. I'm so taken aback; who shakes with the left hand and doesn't she know I can't use it?

Noticing my bewildered expression, my new occupational therapist smiles and hands me what appears to be a large white oven mitt. "For the next three weeks, you are to wear this mitt on your right hand and only remove it for a two-handed task," she says.

Well f**k.

I mean I knew what I had signed up for—an intensive constraint-induced movement therapy program to rehabilitate my left arm poststroke—but even though I *kind of* knew what I was getting myself into, it still came as a shock to hear I couldn't use my good arm at all. I had relied on that arm on to carry me through the everyday tasks of living for the past two years. But now I was being told I couldn't use it. *How on earth was I going to get through these three weeks?*

It wasn't until I suffered a serious brain injury myself that I realized how widespread and common strokes can be, and not just for the elderly. According to the Center for Disease Control and Prevention, strokes kill about 140,000 Americans every year, and about 795,000 people suffer strokes annually.[1] *And I was one of those people.*

Growing up, I knew that strokes were somewhat common, but I had always assumed that the only people they could affect were my grandparents' age. But in reality, stroke is the fifth leading cause of death in the United States and a major cause of disabilities.[2] It is a common misconception that strokes only happen to older people and that anyone under the age of fifty is safe from the risk factors. This is simply not true, and I am living proof of that.

I suffered a stroke at the age of twenty-two, right after I graduated from college.

I decided to write this book as a way to share my story and insights from my recovery to help others and shed light on the reality of life after stroke. My goal is to educate friends,

---

1   "Stroke Facts | Cdc.Gov." 2020. *Cdc.Gov.* https://www.cdc.gov/stroke/facts.htm.

2   "Stroke | Cdc.Gov." 2020. *Cdc.Gov.* https://www.cdc.gov/stroke/index.htm.

family, caregivers, and other stroke survivors by sharing what strategies have worked for me.

For the first two years following my stroke, the last thing I wanted to do was connect with other survivors and engage in the stroke and brain injury community. I hated that this happened to me, and I tried to distance myself from my brain hemorrhage as much as I could. I didn't want my stroke to define me, and so I tried to disengage.

But like fellow stroke survivor and creator of Stroke TV, Aaron Avila, says, "Stroke doesn't define me as a person. How I respond does."

HOW I RESPOND

I'm on a mission to fully embrace this sentiment and respond to my situation in the best and most positive way I can. Pushed around in my wheelchair, I hated how people looked at me. All I wanted was my old life back. In my mind, I was still the same person. Just because I'd suffered a stroke didn't mean I didn't still like to do the same things I did before. But the stark realization that I could not get back the life I once had was a really hard pill to swallow. And as much as I didn't want to admit it, once I accepted my new reality, the question became, "What am I going to do moving forward?"

My ultimate goal early on in my rehab was to reach a point where people I met would not know or suspect I'd had a stroke. But to get to that point, I had a really *(really)* long way to go.

We all face different challenges, and I hope that by sharing mine I can inspire you to find new ways to positively reframe your perspective to better handle whatever challenge you might be facing. You will learn how I was able to:

- Build my balance and learn to walk again
- Learn how to use my left arm and hand again (and I was a lefty before my stroke)
- Adapt to the fact that I lost half of my left peripheral vision
- Retrain my cognitive abilities—recover my memory, attention to detail, vocal inflection
- Get rid of my wheelchair and cane!

My stroke does not define me, but it was a major event that has shaped my perspective on life. It is still hard to remember sometimes, but for the most part I am much better now at being kind to myself, realizing how far I have come in such a short time, and acknowledging the fact that recovery is a lifelong process. I will always be working to improve my mobility, and one of the most important shifts in thinking I underwent was recognizing that just because I can't do everything like I used to doesn't mean I can't still live a full and exciting life.

In this book, I aim to show you that recovery is primarily a state of mind, and that with the right attitude, you will surprise yourself with what is possible. Whether you are recovering from a stroke, looking to change jobs, or finally making the move to a new city, implementing a "fully recovered mindset" will benefit you. The mindset and attitude I have learned over the past few years while going through rehab have revolutionized my thought process and take on life. I hope that by sharing my story and what I've learned, I can empower you to make little changes that will have a huge impact on your quality of life. Onward!

PART 1:

OBSTACLES ARE OPPORTUNITIES

CHAPTER 2

SHIT HAPPENS

———

"But I don't get it. You're too young to have had a stroke," exclaimed my very frazzled Uber driver. "You look like you're doing so well all things considered. It must not have been that bad."

Not been that bad? I wanted to scream. *You have no f**king idea.* People I meet tend to assume that since I'm walking, talking, and moving on my own, everything is fine and my recovery must not have been too involved. Little do they know. With any stroke patient, there is so much more than meets the eye. You have no idea what anyone is really going through, and I've learned how important it is to keep an open mind when engaging in conversation with others. Just because we may not see it doesn't mean the people we engage with aren't facing their own individual battles.

* * *

Two short years ago, I would have hated receiving a comment like that. The whole situation was simply too recent and close to me, and I wanted nothing to do with my traumatic injury.

Now that there is a little more distance between me and the event of my brain hemorrhage, I feel more comfortable fielding questions or comments like this and turning them into an opportunity to educate others on the reality of what it means to live post-brain injury as well as sharing how I've adapted to my new life.

The stroke and brain injury community is small, yet surprisingly well-connected. I have made some amazing fellow survivor friends since I started putting myself out there in the community, but it wasn't until about two years after my stroke that I started doing so. And now I wonder, *What took me so long? How had I gotten by for so long without this incredible support system?*

I had spent the past couple of years with one sole focus: to rehabilitate my arm and leg and get back to all the normal things a twenty-something should be doing, like working a full-time job and complaining about it with my friends over Sunday brunch. I wanted desperately to be like my peers, living with friends in the city. I didn't want to be stuck at home with my parents (as much as I love them) and be dependent on their care.

It felt like my life was blowing right past me and I had no control over the passage of time. I felt fairly confident that at some point I'd be able to live on my own and do the things I used to, but when? And to what extent? I was sick and tired of being home, without a job, and reliant on my parents to ensure I completed the daily tasks of living like eating and bathing. I felt I was missing out on acceptance into some awesome elite club for able, working adults. I desperately wanted to be working like many other young people my age. But before I could do that, I had a few internal questions I needed to resolve.

* * *

Sometimes life is great, everything is going your way, and you feel on top of the world. When I graduated from Georgetown University in May of 2017, I felt like I could do anything. I walked down Healy Lawn the morning of May 20, 2017 to receive my diploma and reap the fruits of a rigorous yet fulfilling academic career. I then proceeded to celebrate (maybe a bit too much) with all my best friends and family.

You could say I was living my very best life. I was so excited to turn the page and begin a new chapter. College was great, but postgrad life would be even better. I had a job lined up in Boston that I was excited about, and three months to relax, travel, and catch up with friends before I made the big move.

It was the perfect scenario. But sometimes when things are going exceptionally well, it feels like the universe wants to spite us and show us that, ultimately, we don't always have control over our situation. It can change at any moment. In other words, shit happens, and sometimes the transpiring situation is out of our control.

Barely a week after I shook Georgetown President DeGioia's hand and received my diploma, my life as I knew it changed forever.

On May 30, 2017, I checked into New York Presbyterian Hospital for brain surgery. Since childhood, I was plagued with terrible migraines, culminating in a series lasting over twenty days when I was in high school.

My neurologist decided to order a magnetic resonance imaging (MRI), which confirmed our suspicions that there was something else going on. We discovered I had a rare arteriovenous malformation (AVM), in the right occipital lobe of my brain. After consulting with many doctors, I made the decision to have brain surgery once I graduated college to remove the risk of a potential rupture. I was informed that with each year of life, an increased chance of the AVM bleeding was possible and could cause a stroke or even death.

I wasn't a huge fan of the idea of brain surgery, but I was even less of a fan of dying from an AVM bleed, so I decided to go in for brain surgery and have the AVM removed. The doctors told me that if everything went well, I would rest and recover for a month or two and be in perfect condition to move up to Boston and start my new job at the end of the summer.

Well, let's just say *that* didn't happen as planned. While in the hospital, one of the preoperative procedures caused a blood clot in my brain, which burst, triggering a massive brain hemorrhage. Suddenly unconscious, I was immediately rushed into an emergency surgery.

My neurosurgeon was paged back to the hospital to operate. He had been on his way home to rest up before my operation the following morning when he got the call. *Guess he wouldn't be getting that good night's sleep, after all.* On his way into surgery, the neurosurgeon told my parents, "The situation is grim. This doesn't look good, but I'll do my best." Then he ran off to the OR.

Seven hours and six liters of blood transfusions later, I lay, completely paralyzed on the left side of my body, in a hospital bed in the New York Presbyterian ICU. Upon waking up from a coma a few hours later, I had no idea what had happened, and even less of an idea what recovery from this might look like.

I then spent a grueling fifteen days in the ICU, mostly on my back. It took all my strength to merely sit up for five minutes. After two weeks, I built up enough strength to be transferred to Kessler Institute, a subacute rehab hospital in West Orange, New Jersey. By the end of my five weeks inpatient, I could walk with a cane (just barely) and was ready to move back home and start outpatient therapy.

Fast forward two years, and I am still learning how to do all the things I once took for granted, like walking and using my left arm and hand, but I have made miraculous progress. While going through rehabilitation, I had a conversation with one of my former Georgetown professors and good friends, Eric Koester. He encouraged me to use my time while rehabbing to engage myself cognitively by writing a book and use it as a way to explore interests I'd never had the time to explore before. After all, when was I ever going to have this much free time, with no obligations apart from (literally) getting back on my feet? I wasn't able to work a full-time job yet, and I had some blocks of time to fill. You can only practice exercises for so many hours of the day.

So, I sat down and did some brainstorming. I thought long and hard about what my interests were and where I wanted to see myself in a few years. And, surprise, surprise, it was *not* confined to a wheelchair or even using a cane.

In college, I overcommitted myself with the amount of activities I did. I have always thrived on being busy and under pressure (at least I liked to think), so I was anxious to get back to feeling like a productive, contributing member of society. Writing a book seemed like the perfect opportunity.

After some brainstorming (and frantic phone calls with my professor Eric), I decided to learn what I could about fashion, a casual, but long-term interest of mine. I interviewed entrepreneurs, writers, models, and business owners to learn whatever I could about the industry. I condensed all my interviews and takeaways into a book, which was published in September 2018, called *Fashion Fwd: How Today's Culture Shapes Tomorrow's Fashion.* I wrote about where I saw the fashion industry heading with the hopes of using my book as a vehicle for expanding my professional network in an industry I cared about and as a tool to unlock potential career opportunities.

That conversation with my professor Eric, in which he encouraged me to *just go for it*, was hands-down the best piece of advice I ever received. I am so grateful that Eric pushed me to make the most of my time while recovering. I can't even begin to imagine what my life would be like now had I *not* written two books. And had my life gone according to plan after I graduated, I doubt I would have set time aside to write two books. So in many ways, my stroke was a blessing; because of it I was able to re-evaluate my priorities and interests.

In my first book, interspersed with the fashion interviews I conducted, I also wove in anecdotes from my experience with stroke rehabilitation. I shared how the act of writing and publishing a book was a form of therapy for me in and of itself. Because ultimately, my book had a more selfish motive. I was writing a book to stimulate myself cognitively in a way that simply going to therapy wouldn't.

I received feedback from that book that my readers enjoyed the personal stories I shared, so I was inspired to go through the process again, this time writing a book on my experience with recovery and what I've learned during my rehabilitation process. I would interview doctors and other patients who have experienced similar challenges. I aim to use this book, my blog (maddistrokeofluck.com), and Instagram account (@maddistrokeofluck) to educate others on the challenges of life poststroke and brain injury as well as share strategies of living. I hope to inspire and empower you to find the courage to repurpose your life and find renewed meaning in the face of whatever challenges life throws your way.

I feel so fortunate to receive such quality rehabilitation and have such amazing therapists who have been fully invested in my recovery. But I know so many people are less fortunate and don't have access to quality therapy programs or care. I have a greater appreciation now for life as a gift and each day as a blessing, and I would like to work my hardest with the time I have been given back to make a difference for others who have experienced brain injury.

Obstacles are opportunities, and I think this crazy obstacle of mine may just be a blessing in disguise, a beautiful opportunity to repurpose and make a positive impact in the lives of others. My main motivation for writing this book was to share my experience and biggest takeaways from stroke rehab for the benefit of others.

Over the past few years, I've grappled with a lot of huge questions, like what did it mean that I had a stroke and what did it imply for my future? My whole world is different now, and I wondered what that meant for how I was to live my life moving forward. So, one day I decided I would turn my traumatic situation into the best thing that ever happened to me.

PART 2:

NEW PRIORITIES

CHAPTER 3

SHI(F)T HAPPENS

———

"How can you stay so positive given what happened to you?" I am often asked. The answer is simply no other option exists. I've always been a very positive person, but I actually feel that my positivity amplified after my stroke. I know so many people who have suffered a stroke and struggle to see the good side, but I also know a lot of people who choose to view each day as a gift like I do. I've surrounded myself with a network of hard-working and optimistic people and I think that has made all the difference.

We may not be able to control what happens to us, but we can control how we react to what happens to us. I had something terrible happen to me that was out of my control, but what was definitely well within my control was my response. So, how was I going to process and respond to such a traumatic event? I had to shift my attitude and embrace positivity.

* * *

Sometimes, it can be hard to talk to people that I know but haven't seen since before the stroke. They don't know what to expect from me. Everyone has their own perceptions of what it means to have a stroke, and a lot of times those perceptions are wrong. For me, I've noticed that my perspective shift since my injury manifests itself in how I interact with others.

Communication is an important skill for anyone, and I've noticed that after having a brain injury, the way I communicate with others has changed. This isn't necessarily a bad thing; in fact, I would argue that it is for the better. The old me was terrible at keeping in touch with distant friends and family. In college, my mom would always complain that it was impossible to get ahold of me because I never responded to her texts or calls. *Terrible daughter,* I know. I don't know what I was doing; I guess I figured I had more important things to do and my family could wait until they were done. But tomorrow is not a guarantee and we have to let those who are important to us know how much they mean to us every time we get the chance because we don't know when the time will come that they are no longer around. Let me say that again—*let the ones you love know it, every second you get.*

But alas, I have since changed my ways, and now I make it a priority to keep in touch with those I care about. I'm not exactly sure what prompted this change, but I guess there's nothing quite like almost dying to get you to appreciate what you previously took for granted.

* * *

I am the luckiest girl on earth because after my near-death scare, I had people from all walks of life come out to support me: family, friends, acquaintances, and even people I didn't know all around the world were praying for my recovery.

There's something quite powerful about that. People all over the world were thinking of me and sending positive thoughts for my recovery. And I didn't even know all of them. But quite frankly, these prayers and positive thoughts from those I knew and loved as well as strangers completely changed the trajectory of my recovery. The amount of prayer cards, home-cooked dinners, gifts, and letters was absolutely overwhelming.

There's also nothing quite like a stroke to bring you closer to those you had drifted apart from. When I was in the hospital, I was paid visits from many friends, and I don't even remember most of them. At that point in time, I was completely "out of it" and had no idea what was going on.

My best friend, Freddy, came to visit me in the hospital soon after the operation. I was lying in the ICU with a drain attached to my head to monitor the swelling and drain the blood in my brain. On this day, Freddy came to visit the hospital from Washington, DC, and sat beside me. I asked him if he could rip off the constraints that were holding my hands down and remove the drain because it was annoying.

Bad idea, I know. But at that point I wanted nothing more than to be free of the restraints. Unfortunately, my parents and the nurses forbade him from going through with it. Had they not been there or said something, I'm sure he would have obliged, being the amazing friend that he is. I felt so restricted being strapped down to my bed with no way to move. And even if I wanted to move my left arm or leg, it was impossible. I had absolutely no ability to move anything on my left side.

Not only did I have no movement on the entire left side of my body, but I also had no sensation on that side, either. In the first few days after surgery, the surgeon would come into my room and ask if I could feel where he was touching me on my arm or leg. I couldn't. So yeah, *we've got some major problems.*

From when I was in the hospital to inpatient subacute rehab, to outpatient therapy, you can say I have been blessed to receive the support of countless people. I have been truly humbled by the care and kindness of everyone I've interacted with since the stroke. I know it meant a lot to my family that people out there were praying for me and cheering me on, as well as helping my family in whatever way they could.

When I had the stroke in the hospital, my younger sister, Bridget, was at her senior prom. When she found out about what had just happened to me, our good family friend graciously rushed her to the hospital so she could wait for me to get out of surgery. It's the things like that for which I am especially grateful.

The fact that I even have a support system, let alone an amazingly magnanimous and extensive one, is truly heartwarming. I know many people out there who suffer strokes or brain injuries have no one to look out for them. Some of my older friends I made in rehab had partners who left them after years of marriage because they couldn't cope with what happened.

At first, I thought, *well gee, that's dumb. They're not the ones who actually suffered through the experience.* But now, upon further reflection, I sort of get it. People cope with obstacles in very different ways, and maybe some people just don't know how to process, so they pull away.

To be honest, I was shocked to find that some friends of mine never once reached out to check in on me even after they learned what happened. When I tried to get in touch with them after I was in a better headspace, I received no response. *Radio silence.* Essentially, I was being ghosted by my former friends. So that sucked, but I've learned it does no good to dwell on the bad, when we have so much to live for.

Even more than those who ghosted me, I was overwhelmed by the support that I *did* receive. This encouraged me to focus on the people who actually cared and not waste my time worrying about those who couldn't find it within themselves to check in. Because I could only do so much. I couldn't force someone to want to talk with me or spend time with me.

And that is one of the biggest lessons I learned during my recovery. As much as I hated to admit it, I knew I had to let some things and people go so I could focus on the people who really did care about me. But that was easier said than done.

For a long time, I held on to the glimmer of hope that one day these people I once called good friends would come around. But when many months of unsolicited responses passed, I knew I needed a major mental shift. And the thing was, I knew what I had to change. It was simple; I just needed to stop caring about people who wouldn't reciprocate so I could move on with my life, focusing on those who did care about me.

It took a long time, but after many months of telling myself to just let it go, I finally got over it. I know people come and go in life. And not everyone cares for you and looks out for you the way that you do for yourself. It's a lesson my mom worked hard to instill in me after having a stroke. *No one will look out for you as much as me and your dad do,* she said. *You need to always look out for yourself.*

I think she's right. My parents have supported me from day one, always there to assist when help is needed. Which is great because I have a lot more problems poststroke that some people meeting me for the first time might not realize initially. Like my spasticity problems.

CHAPTER 4

IT'S NOT JUST FOR WRINKLES

———

"Are you ready? It will just be a little prick," my physiatrist warned. "Thanks for the heads up," I joked. *Prick*, the needle penetrated my left trapezius, and Dr. Jasey turned the switch on the funny little contraption sitting in front of us, which started to hum faintly. "This is how we figure out where to inject," he said. "The louder the noise from the machine, the more active the muscle is." *That's kind of cool*, I remember thinking. *So, we listen to the muscle to get a sense of where the spasticity and tone is most prominent and inject.*

But as cool as it sounded in theory, the reality was this was more than just a little prick, says the girl who has always had a remarkably high tolerance for pain. Even as a child, I was never scared of getting shots. After all, it was just a needle. In and out, right? Well, if you've ever gotten Botox, you know it's not so simple. The needle goes in, and *stays* in until the doctor has located the correct muscle and injected. For me, the whole process could take an hour's time. But it helped. A lot.

Prior to having a stroke, I had no idea that Botox was used for anything other than cosmetic alterations, but since I began getting injections, I have seen the toxin work wonders for me in terms of spasticity management. The injections begin to take effect after a week, and essentially paralyze the over-active muscles in my leg, arm, hand, and neck. When my muscles are in a weakened state, I'm able to focus on training them more. The muscle tone that often causes my muscles to involuntarily contract is temporarily out of commission.

The first time I got Botox, I was skeptical, but my arm, hand, neck, and leg were so tight that I was willing to try anything. Because of the muscle tone in my arm and hand, I wore a splint so that my fingers stayed straight and in a good position. I also sported an ugly neck collar to keep my neck and head in a good position so my cervical dystonia wouldn't get worse. Unfortunately, because of the stroke, my neck was all messed up and I couldn't even bring my head to midline. I had problems on top of problems, and the idea was that the neck collar and hand splint would help.

I hated it. The splint, the neck collar, the muscle tightness, all of it. It was so annoying adjusting to the fact that my fingers wouldn't listen to what I wanted them to do. They clenched into a fist on their own. It was the weirdest thing; I couldn't control my arm or hand movements. In fact, I couldn't control anything on my whole left side at all.

* * *

Prior to having a stroke, I was what one would call the happy-go-lucky type. I was spontaneous, impulsive, and had a genuine appreciation for the present moment. I can't tell you how many times a friend called me up on the weekend asking if I wanted to do some crazy new and exciting activity. To which more often than not I responded—*of course!* I was always on the hunt for a brand-new experience.

After my stroke, all of this changed. The fun and spontaneous, happy-go-lucky girl I had been was gone. I woke up in a hospital bed groggy, confused, and unaware of how to go on. I was paralyzed. Life sucked. I just wanted my old life back.

I know we can't completely have control over what happens in life, but we do have control over how we respond to the challenges thrown our way. For me, my shift in perspective poststroke made me much more appreciative of the moment. Because let's face it, shi(f)t happens. And like I said, it's not like I was unappreciative of it before, it's just that now my life had an added layer of meaning. Nothing quite like almost dying to get you to really appreciate what you have and not take anything for granted. Literally.

* * *

I remember distinctly the moment when I decided I couldn't just accept my situation and I had to take control of my future. I was inpatient at Kessler, learning how to walk with a quad cane. A quad cane is a mobility device similar to the straight cane but with a metal base and four protruding feet for stability. Typically, after therapy, I practiced walking up and down the halls with my cane and the help one of my parents or siblings (and my wheelchair to rest in for a break).

On one such day, my brother, Charlie, and I were walking (more like trudging) down the hall. I hated these walks; they were hard, and a part of me felt like asking, *why bother?* My left ankle was wrapped in an ACE bandage to help with my foot drop until I had an AFO brace specially made for my foot.

That's right. Because of my stroke I now suffered from a condition where I couldn't lift the front part of my foot, due to weakness/paralysis of the anterior muscles. So for now, I managed by wrapping my foot in an ACE bandage to facilitate a heel-toe strike.

My brother and I stopped in front of an open door to rest (back then I could only walk about twenty feet or so before I needed a rest break) and at this moment, sitting in my wheelchair, I thought, *what am I doing?* I looked into the open room in front of me to see a patient who was completely paralyzed from the neck down lying in bed. At this moment I thought, "Yes I can't walk far, but I *can* walk," and that in and of itself is a huge blessing. Yes, I have to take breaks every couple of feet because I'm tired, but I *can* stand up and take that step. If I kept working at it, I was only going to improve. How much, no one could say, but I knew I had to put in the work to find out and just keep putting one foot in front of the other.

Every day, I think about how the neurosurgeon told my family that my situation was grim, and he couldn't guarantee my survival, but he was going to do everything he could. When I think about that, I'm reminded of how lucky I am to still be on this earth. Each day of life on this planet seems like a bonus chance to me, an extra special opportunity to work toward my goals.

This change in perspective has affected virtually everything in my life—my relationships with the people I know and meet, and even my relationship with myself. It's a shame it took a near-death experience for me to have a fuller appreciation of the present moment and recognize the amazing gift I have been given. I have been blessed with this incredible opportunity to work hard and recover, and I owe it to myself and everyone I interact with to give it my best shot. I can't do most things like I used to, but maybe that is also a blessing in disguise. Maybe this experience is the perfect chance for me to redefine my priorities and figure out what is truly important to me.

CHAPTER 5

A WHOLE NEW WORLD

———

"Did you not see that woman there?" my mom scolded me seconds after I collided with a passerby on the street. "You ran right into her."

"I didn't see her," I responded. "She was on your left side," my mom sighed. "You've *got* to turn your head to scan and look to the left. There's a whole world over there that you're missing."

While for me my stroke deficits mainly manifested in the physical, I did also suffer a severe loss of peripheral vision, which is never coming back. So, I need to learn to adjust to this new normal. Adjusting to my new life and recultivating the skills I once took for granted, like spatial awareness, has been a huge challenge. But I'm making the most of it (or trying to).

What many "normies" (normal, non-stroke associated folks) don't understand about us survivors is that we may have a lot more issues than what first meets the eye. There's usually always more to the story than what is blatantly visible, which is one of the main reasons why I enjoy sharing my story and educating others about stroke and brain injury. Every recovery is different, but I think the more we share to educate others, the more they will be aware of what could be and how to prevent it or deal with it if it does happen.

For the first few months after my stroke, I didn't know that my lack of vision and proprioceptive awareness could be such a big deal. I suffered from something known as spatial neglect. Spatial neglect basically implies a lack of awareness on one side. I had damage primarily to the right side of my brain, so I was left-side affected, and, therefore, suffered from left-side neglect. Left neglect is defined as a lack of attention to and awareness of the left side and is a common side effect of stroke.[3]

My parents were the ones who first realized my left neglect when I was at inpatient subacute rehab. At mealtimes, I only ate the food on the right side of my plate. Weird, right? When I was done eating, my mom would turn to me and ask, "Are you sure you got everything on the plate?" To which I answered, "Obviously!" "Look again," she'd say. And when I looked again and saw no food on the plate, she would shift the food to my right side and I immediately saw what I had missed. My mom even began intentionally placing my dessert on the left side of my plate to force me to scan because she knew I couldn't say no to a chocolate chip cookie.

---

3 "Left Side Neglect Following Stroke — There Is More to the Picture". 2020. *Neurorehabdirectory.Com.* https://www.neurorehabdirectory. com/left-side-neglect-following-stroke-picture/.

As you can imagine, this lack of awareness was a big problem. Yes, I had lost a lot of vision, but my eyes still worked and there was nothing wrong with them. The problem was neurologic; my brain wasn't recognizing my whole left side or field of vision. It's literally like opening your eyes and only seeing what's directly in front of you, and nothing peripherally. My vision just suddenly cut off on the left, and there was nothing there.

Because I had lost the majority of my left-sided peripheral vision, I couldn't see anything out of the corner of my eye. For me to see something, it had to be right in front of me. And this has been a massive problem for me since the stroke because I have to remember to constantly turn my head and scan to make sure I see everything. And I *wasn't* seeing everything. There was so much happening over on the left side that I was simply ignoring. It's kind of like, *if a tree falls in the middle of the woods and no one sees it, did it even happen?*

Except in this case, unfortunately it *did* happen. Just because I didn't see her doesn't mean there wasn't a person there that I just collided with.

Left neglect is a weird phenomenon and one that is definitely challenging to deal with. I'm still not completely adjusted. When I'm out walking with my parents, on occasion my mom will have to say something to remind me to continuously look over to my left side. It's weird for me to need reminders to do something I've done seamlessly my entire life and never even given a second thought to doing. Remember to scan over to the left side? Shouldn't that just come naturally?

Maybe not anymore, but with practice my sense of awareness is improving.

By practicing, I mean remembering to physically turn my head to the left side. When I do, a whole new world opens up to me. Pretend, for instance, we were sitting at a table and you were across from me, but positioned slightly off to the left. I would never see you unless I turned my head. Since I also had neck problems, I was less inclined to turn my neck. And since I wasn't always remembering to scan, I had to make sure I was using all my other senses to help me be aware. I never knew there could be so many problems from suffering a brain injury.

I am also convinced that the Botox injections I get have helped tremendously with this scanning problem. Not because it improved my awareness but because it loosened my neck muscles to make it easier to turn my head to the left. With a paralyzed sternocleidomastoid muscle, turning became easier and better range of neck motion equated to better spatial awareness.

CHAPTER 6

WHAC-A-MOLE

Did you ever play that game Whac-A-Mole as a kid? It's that game where the little critters pop up and you have to swing a mallet to hit all of them before time runs out. Super fun. I used to love to play that game as a child and was pretty good at it too, if I do say so myself.

But little did eight-year-old Maddi know that at age twenty-four she'd be channeling that Whac-A-Mole passion to help in her recovery from brain injury. During a three-week occupational therapy stint in Birmingham, Alabama, I tackled the dreaded Dynavision board and worked on my visual scanning. The Dynavision board was pegged up on the wall and had about fifty switches all across it. When the switches illuminated, my job was to hit them like Whac-A-Mole with a mallet tied securely on my left hand. Sounds entertaining, right? But it was really quite challenging. While this was definitely an exercise in using my left arm to hit the light switches on the Dynavision board, it was even more so an exercise in improving my visual scanning to make sure I noticed everything on the board.

For a straight year and a half of my life, I juggled physical and occupational outpatient therapy with cognitive rehab. As much as I hated to admit it, cognitive therapy was especially important for me to improve my visual scanning, memory, and attention to detail. I knew I had issues when my therapist gave me a sheet with a bunch of letters on it one day and asked me to cross out all the c's and e's. *Easy enough*, I thought. Wrong. After completing the exercise and scanning each column one by one to cross off the correct letters, I was surprised to learn that I still had missed about 30 percent of the letters. *How had I not been able to see them?* I realized then that I had been in denial of my cognitive deficiencies, refusing to accept my new reality and instead living under the false assumption that my old way of doing things would still work for me. But my old life was gone and things are different now. I face a new reality, and new struggles. Visual scanning is one of them.

I tried anything and everything to improve my visual scanning. And with constant practice, attention to detail, and a lot of head-turning, I began to make improvements. Simply making an attempt, regardless of the outcome, is the most helpful thing you can do for yourself when retraining your brain to do what it once did without a second thought. Sure, you might not be able to cross off all the correct letters from a piece of paper or remember a list of numbers rattled off to you, but you sure as heck are never going to get better at it if you don't make an attempt.

The Dynavision board exercise was tough for me, but the more I did it the faster I got, and the fewer mistakes I made. Moral of the story: don't give up and keep getting after it.

Find ways to incorporate therapy constantly into your daily life. Each moment of every day presents us with a unique set of circumstances and choices, and it is up to us to decide what we are going to make of it and how we are going to live our lives.

Think about it like this: assuming you live until your eightieth birthday, you've been on this earth for 2,522,880,000 seconds. And you probably spent roughly a third of that time sleeping. So, that leaves you with about 168,19,20,000 waking seconds. And after those seconds are exhausted, that's that.

I don't know what comes after life on this earth, but I do know that the life we have is happening now. Not tomorrow, not yesterday, but now. And *now* is all we ever have. So, how will we spend our precious time? Will we constantly push our limits to recover use of our affected side poststroke or dwell on our struggles and feel sorry for ourselves?

With practice, my visual scanning improved, but not enough where I felt totally confident with my ability to navigate crowded venues and uneven terrain completely on my own. One of the main barriers I faced that prevented me from living the life I so desperately wanted was my neck issues. Tightness in my left SCM, trapezius, scalene, longissimus, levator, you name it. Any and every muscle running through my neck and shoulder was tight. Because of my stroke, I suffered a bad case of cervical dystonia, a painful condition that caused my neck muscles to contract involuntarily. My neck was so tight after my stroke that initially I couldn't even bring my head to midline. It seemed to be stuck in a position tilted to the side. This was bad because it affected my ability to see.

So, I had a neck condition that not only caused me headaches but impacted my vision as well. No wonder I was running into signs on the street. I was missing a significant portion of my peripheral vision and couldn't turn my neck well enough to the side to compensate. And in addition, I suffered from double vision, which made it difficult for me to focus. I couldn't wear contacts; I had to wear special glasses with prism lenses that helped my brain register the images I saw through them as one. My doctors also told me I had rotated vertebrae in my neck that contributed to my problem.

So to fix my neck, I tried everything. I saw a chiropractor and an acupuncture specialist, which definitely helped, but my saving grace came in the form of a DO who specialized in osteopathic manipulation.

CHAPTER 7

PAIN IN THE NECK

———

"Why don't you try seeing a doctor that specializes in osteopathy for your neck?" my physiatrist recommended at one appointment some months after my stroke. I didn't know what another doctor could possibly prescribe that could help, but at this point I was willing to try anything. Things could only get better, right?

At my first appointment with my new doctor, I rolled in (literally, I was still using a transport chair at the time to get places since my walking endurance with the cane wasn't too good yet) with no idea of what to expect. At that first appointment, I was surprised to learn that no medication prescriptions would be involved with the appointment. Instead, my new doctor planned to work on my neck through manipulation. The osteopathic manipulation my doctor practiced was a more hands-on technique to relieve pain. Since I had a lot of neck pain and rotated vertebrae, my doctor had proposed this form of treatment as a solution.

I'm so glad she did because it has worked wonders for me. When I started visiting Dr. Klingmeyer and her cohort of amazingly talented doctors for osteopathic manipulation, my entire head and neck were stuck in a tilted position. It was not pretty. If you had seen me then, you would have instantly been able to tell something on a neurologic level was not right.

Osteopathic manipulative treatment involves gentle pressure on the muscles and joints to relieve pain. At the time of this writing, I am two and a half years post stroke, and successfully able to turn my head all the way to the left side. (I just need to get accustomed to actually doing it more!) My head is much more centered on my neck and I no longer have bad muscle pain.

Dr. Klingmeyer has supported me throughout my journey with recovery. I have been seeing her and her colleagues about once a month for two years now to work on my neck problems. Because of the manipulative treatments, my neck has improved to the point that I no longer experience pain or headaches from the cervical dystonia. My head can reach midline, and I'm working on getting more comfortable with compensating for my vision loss by actually turning my head. I owe much of my recovery to these amazing doctors.

I fully realize how lucky I am to have such an incredible support system to help me throughout my rehabilitation. According to Dr. Klingmeyer, family support is the most important thing for recovery. And after that, "positivity— there's a lot of psychosocial factors that go into a recovery because it's mentally draining. So being able to keep up that good mood, and even if you're down, being able to bounce back and say, 'You know what, I'm down today, but tomorrow,

I'm going to get back on the train and start my physical therapy again, or what have you.'"[4]

I think her insight into the role of attitude in recovery is crucial and emphasizes the fact that more factors are at play than what one might see on the surface level. The important thing is that, no matter how bad things are or how far away you feel you may be from your goals, you jump back in and keep pushing forward.

I am extremely grateful to have met Dr. Klingmeyer and the other doctors in her office. My doctors encouraged me to believe in myself and believe I was capable of getting past this. It's crazy what a simple shift in mindset can do. Here's to continued progress—onward and upward!

---

4   Dr. Dorothy Klingmeyer, conversation with the author, 22 June 2019.

CHAPTER 8

ADJUSTING TO
THE NEW YOU

———

I have always been THE most impulsive person I know. Since childhood, I've had a tendency to rush into things without properly thinking them through. Act now, rationalize and figure out logistics later type of thing. Any activity, you name it: a spontaneous beach weekend with friends, an impulsive hot summer's day swim in what turns out to be a leech-infested river. Okay, so I didn't say I was the *smartest* risk-taker, but this impulsive mentality usually served me well. I had fun.

* * *

After my stroke, all of this changed. Poststroke, I'm no longer as impulsive as I once was and find I need to budget more time to plan activities.

But that's okay. As stroke and brain injury survivors, we have a very unique experience that shows our ability to adapt and make the most of challenges. I can't do most things like I used to, but I can try and discover new ways to accomplish tasks. I refuse to fall victim to complacency and accept my situation, and I want to push myself beyond the realm of perceived possibility and see what I am truly capable of.

And look just how far I've come.

CHAPTER 9

POSITIVE HEALTH

"If I were in your situation, I don't think I'd have the strength within me to see the positive," I've been told. To which I respond, "Of course you would! You'd have no other choice." You don't give yourself enough credit, and you're *much* stronger than you think you are. You just don't know it until something like this happens and really tests you.

As I have learned from going through stroke rehab myself, the role of attitude and resilience in recovery is 90 percent of the battle. Dr. Machteld Huber, a researcher at the Bolk Institute in the Netherlands, understood this as well and made it her life's work to redefine health. She came up with the concept of "positive health," which is referred to as the "ability to adapt and self-manage, in light of the physical, emotional, and social challenges of life."[5] I like this definition because it implies that even if I am unable to write or type on the computer like I used to, I could still be considered in good health.

---

5   "Louis Bolk Instituut – Positive Health". 2020. *Louisbolk.Org*. http://www.louisbolk.org/health-nutrition/integrative-medicine-3/new-concept-of-health.

The present definition of the World Health Organization (WHO) is that "health is the state of complete physical, mental and social well-being and not merely the absence of diseases or infirmity."[6] This definition is far from ideal because it is static and does not account for attitude and mental resilience in recovery. Similar to what Ella Sofia, a fellow stroke survivor and habit coach, told me, recovery entails much more than ability or inability. It is not so black and white. "We created a more dynamic concept, which is about resilience and about being able to deal with your illness and integrate it in your life," said Dr. Huber.[7] Meaning that even if we are not at 100 percent of our ability, we can still be considered healthy and lead a fulfilling life.

This is good news for me because I have finally reached a point where I feel (for the most part), that my physical and visual impairments aren't preventing me from living my best life. I have new limits and can't handle as much as I used to before the fatigue hits like a brick wall, but that doesn't stop me from making the most of the present moment.

Dr. Huber and Van Vliet published an article in 2016 elaborating on this new concept of positive health. According to their publication, positive health also encompasses "dimensions such as social participation, quality of life and daily functioning. Hence it considers not only medical treatment

---

6   "Frequently Asked Questions". 2020. *Who.Int.* https://www.who.int/ about/who-we-are/frequently-asked-questions.

7   "Louis Bolk Instituut – Positive Health". 2020. *Louisbolk.Org.* http:// www.louisbolk.org/health-nutrition/integrative-medicine-3/new-concept-of-health.

but also options for making better use of patients' abilities to cope, adapt and self-manage."[8] So, apart from the physical aspects of health, it is important to also consider our mental and social wellness.

Humans are social beings, and the people we surround ourselves with is so important and has a tremendous impact on our quality of life. You know that saying, "You are the sum of the five people you spend the most time with?" It's true. The people you hang out with influence your thoughts and opinions as well as your outlook on life. You deserve nothing but the greatest life possible, and it all starts with attitude.

8   2020. *Louisbolk.Org.* http://www.louisbolk.org/downloads/3108.pdf.

CHAPTER 10

SUGAR-FREE RASPBERRY, PLEASE

––––––

One of the marvels of the human body and brain is neuroplasticity, or the brain's capacity to rewire itself. A study conducted assessing patients' ability to adapt after having half their brain removed showed that we have way greater capabilities than we may realize. Neuroplasticity was present in these patients who had undergone hemispherectomies (that is, had half their brain removed) as children. A hemispherectomy, which consists of slicing the brain down the middle and removing half, is a procedure done primarily in children who suffer from terrible seizures. The study revealed that, in fact, their ability to adapt and lead "normal" lives was amazing, beyond what they had assumed.[9]

The doctors who conducted this study were surprised at just how well the patients with only half a brain managed to

––––––

9   "People with Half Their Brain Removed Are Doing Surprisingly Well". 2020. *Futurism*. https://futurism.com/neoscope/people-half-brain-removed-doing-well.

recover. "The people with hemispherectomies that we studied were remarkably high-functioning," CalTech researcher Dorit Kliemann, one of the doctors behind the California Institute of Technology study, said. "They have intact language skills. When I put them in the scanner, we made small talk, just like the hundreds of other individuals I have scanned."[10]

Wild, right? The human brain has the incredible ability to reshape itself, and this amazing capacity is something I experienced firsthand during my rehab.

* * *

"Just a hundred more feet. Come on, Maddi, then you can take a rest break," my mom encouraged me. It was a chilly September morning in 2017, and we were getting some steps in at the mall. At this point I was walking with a straight cane, having graduated from the quad cane a couple of months prior. I absolutely hated my cane and just wanted to walk without assistance. But as I know full well, things like this are easier said than done and involve constant work.

As much as I wanted to push through my fatigue and make it to the bench a few yards away, I wasn't sure I could do it. It was so far away, and I was already so tired. When I found myself falling into this cycle of negativity and thoughts of *I*

---

10   "People with Half Their Brain Removed Are Doing Surprisingly Well." 2020. *Futurism*. https://futurism.com/neoscope/people-half-brain-removed-doing-well.

can't, I knew it was time to give myself a little pep talk and turn my attitude around.

But wait, you might be saying to yourself. *How am I supposed to find the will to go on when I'm already so exhausted and can't see the upside to my situation? Is there even a point or a reason to go on?* If this is ever you, then listen up. I'm about to drop some wisdom.

The answer is *yes,* even when times get especially tough, you will always have a reason to go on. You have something incredible, beautiful, and quite frankly, *rare.* You are *alive.* Let me repeat: you are *alive.* If I need to scream it from the mountain top so you hear it, I will because life is such a precious gift, and one that is so easily taken away. It unfortunately took an extremely traumatic situation for me to appreciate that, but I'm so happy it did. Because now when I'm feeling down or don't think I have the will within me to keep going, I stop and remind myself of the blessing I have. Sure, maybe that day at the mall with my cane I was too fatigued to walk to the rest point, but if anything, that gave me a new goal to work toward. I was going to practice walking (even if it had to be with my cane) until I reached a point where I had enough endurance to complete a lap around the mall without rest breaks.

* * *

Which brings me back to neuroplasticity. See, I was committed to positively rewiring my brain so I could handle activities I once enjoyed. My brain wasn't accustomed to walking long distances since my stroke, but I was set on changing that. If I could just show my brain it wasn't that hard and I could do it, I figured my brain would get used to it and then think maybe I could handle more. A lap around the Short Hills Mall, the mall nearest my house, is a little under two thousand steps. While at first, I couldn't make it even halfway around the mall before I needed a break, the more I walked, the stronger my endurance became, and the farther I could walk. Once I ditched my cane for good on September 29, 2017, I suddenly found myself facing a whole host of problems again that I thought I had beaten. Now without my cane, I had to readjust and rebuild my stamina from scratch. If you've ever used a cane yourself, you know that once you transition away from the cane, your stamina reverts back to zero. I was so discouraged; I had worked so hard to build my endurance so I could walk far distances with the cane, and now that I didn't have it anymore, I found that the mental fatigue from walking kicked in quicker.

Although the tiredness settled in faster than it did when I walked with a cane, I knew that it was because my brain had to work harder to get the correct muscles to fire. I couldn't rely anymore on my cane to support me. Without this crutch to rely on, I realized how much cognitive power goes into an activity as "simple" as walking. I would walk a hundred feet and be exhausted, unable to go on. But I didn't experience a physical tiredness; it was cognitive fatigue. My brain was exhausted from working so hard to send the correct message from my brain to my legs to get them to move. It was hard work, but I have never been one to shy away from a challenge. Obstacles are opportunities, and I was going to conquer Short Hills Mall.

* * *

Fast Fwd two months to November 2017. I'm back at the mall without my cane and getting more steps in with my mom. "If you can make it all the way to Nordstrom, we can take a break and I'll buy you a coffee," my mom promised. There we go. This was just the motivation I needed. My mom knew I got tired and frustrated easily, so she was always coming up with new incentives to encourage me to keep going. I love coffee, so this was a hard reward to pass up. *Just think*, I thought, *only three hundred or so steps between you and a sugar-free raspberry iced coffee.* (Sugar-free because I was trying to cut down on my sugar intake.) *You can do this.*

It's honestly amazing what a little bit of incentivized motivation can do. After hearing that, I found myself with renewed energy and sprinted (figuratively, of course), to the Nordstrom Ebar, where my efforts and exertion were rewarded with a much-needed iced coffee.

By the time I left the mall after our November morning stroll, I had 4,500 steps. That was like a world record back then. In the next months, I continued to push for more steps and more movement. Mall walking was absolutely crucial to my recovery and to getting me where I am today. Through continued practice with mall walking, I was able to build up my endurance to the point that I could walk ten-thousand-plus steps with minimal breaks. Every step I took, even when I was exhausted or didn't feel like walking, was one more coin in my brain bank, one more deposit to rewire my brain.

But iced coffee wasn't my only motivation (although it was a big one). I made quite a few new friends while walking at the mall, who constantly encouraged me. Every time I walked by the early morning mall walkers, they'd shout words of encouragement, motivating me to continue on my way. They saw the progress I made, from cane to no cane, and I am thankful for their support.

PART 3:

POSITIVE VIBES ONLY

CHAPTER 11

LIVE YOUR BEST LIFE

———

"You're doing so well in your recovery, and I wanna introduce you to someone. She's young too and hasn't met any other young stroke survivors. She wants to connect more with members of our community," one of my survivor friends told me. I was flattered; one, that he thought I was recovering well, and two that he thought of me as the person he wanted to introduce. I couldn't have been more excited about it. "Of course!" I exclaimed. I jumped at the opportunity to meet a new survivor and share stories.

As I've learned, the stroke and brain injury community is very well-connected. Chatting with people who understand what it's like has been amazing and so helpful. I don't have to explain myself or why I randomly get tired because my friends get it. They're struggling through the same thing. But I wasn't always eager to connect and share my story.

A couple of blocks from my house, someone has a sign on the lawn. It reads, "Don't give up," and on the other side the message is, "You are not alone." I find the sign to be a great reminder to constantly push forward for progress.

* * *

I firmly believe that recovery is in the mindset, and having a positive outlook in the face of challenges is 90 percent of the battle. In the next few chapters, I will explore in more depth the role of positivity in recovery from a traumatic event such as stroke. Feel free to skip around and delve into whatever chapter interests you. I won't be offended by skipping around. I hope the stories I have shared from my own personal experience and the experience of other survivors can help you in some way and empower you to make the most of whatever your situation might be. All situations have a bright side, even a stroke, and it is my mission to help you find it.

* * *

I am not just a stroke survivor; I am a stroke *thriver*. I know that despite my limitations, I am still capable of living a full life. I may not have full use of my left side like I did before, but I'm not going to let that stop me. If there's anything I've learned, it's that recovery is a lifelong process and I will never stop working toward where I want to be.

Life is just a collection of all these hundreds and thousands of present moments that make up who we are today. So, how we spend each moment we are given matters. Sure, we can look back to the past and dream ahead to the future, but we will never get where we want to be unless we put in the work now.

In terms of my recovery, I think this mindset has made all the difference. Connecting with fellow stroke survivors has been an incredibly rewarding experience for me, and I'm so grateful to have the opportunity to help others and be helped by my pre and poststroke friends and family.

I have made insane progress since May 2017, but I still have many big goals ahead. Independent living, travel, cooking, running, and cleaning are just a few of the goals that I'm still working toward. I know that step by step I will get there, by making the most of the moments I have, and treating them as precisely what they are—a gift.

CHAPTER 12

SHARE YOUR STROKE OF GENIUS

———

Kyle Mengelkamp is a fellow stroke survivor based in New York who also thinks it is important to turn one's stroke into a positive. He told me that one day he was at an AT&T contest and sat down next to a woman who immediately asked him his story. Kyle shared with her the story of his stroke and his mission to help other survivors and give back to the community. They exchanged contact information, and late that night Kyle received an email from the woman he met requesting a meeting. "Stroke of genius, what do you say?" she exclaimed as she burst through the door and into the meeting. The rest is history.[11]

The two of them teamed up to ultimately win the AT&T contest with a story on Kyle, and Stroke of Genius was born. The "stroke of genius" being the moment of changed perspective every survivor goes through that changes his or her attitude

---

11   Kyle Mengelkamp, conversation with author, 27 July 2019.

for the better.[12] So they started Share your Stroke of Genius, and now travel the country capturing and sharing the "stories of triumph" of fellow stroke survivors.

The Stroke of Genius is the moment when a person decides how she is going to live the rest of her life. Everything is a choice. Each moment of every day we get to make the choice of how we are going to live our lives. My Stroke of Genius was especially enlightening because it opened my eyes to the fact that all we have is the present moment. I said it once and I'll say it again because it's so important. Each moment of every day presents us with a unique set of circumstances and choices, and it is our decision to make of it what we want. We could choose to see the negative and dwell on our problems, or we could choose to be positive and make the most of our situation.

Ultimately, we decide what kind of life we will live based off of our actions and choices. Dr. Jill Bolte Taylor, author, neuroanatomist, fellow stroke survivor, and speaker of the popular TED Talk and book, *My Stroke of Insight*, made it her mission to learn about the brain and how we process after trauma. Our attitude and energy has an incredible impact on our quality of life, and so Dr. Jill Bolte Taylor says we must, "take responsibility for the energy you bring ... you are a life force power of the universe."[13]

---

12 Kyle Mengelkamp, conversation with author, 27 July 2019.

13 "World Stroke Day Featuring Dr. Jill Bolte Taylor And Claudia Mason". 2020. *Facebook Watch*. https://www.facebook.com/shareyourstrokeofgenius/videos/530693587717508/.

If you survived a stroke or some serious trauma, the question now becomes, *what will you do next?* "This is the gift, right here right now," Dr. Jill Bolte Taylor states. When asked how she was able to be happy after having a stroke, she powerfully states what should be obvious: I didn't die that day. "Simply because I did not die that day, I live in a state of gratitude for the fact that I am still alive," she says.[14]

This is powerful stuff. Dr. Jill Bolte Taylor explains how important it is to reframe and reposition our attitudes after trauma. First comes awareness and acknowledgment of the current state and condition, followed by acceptance and using it to propel you forward. Instead of saying, for instance, it kills me that I can no longer use my hand, we can actively choose to reframe our perspective. We must pay attention to the energy we bring to the room and be aware of how it affects us and others. It's so easy as a stroke survivor to fall into the cycle of blaming and saying *woe is me, why did this happen to me?* But Dr. Taylor says that thoughts like these are our left hemisphere speaking, and when the anxiety rises, we have a choice to make. We could let it get the best of us, or we could take a minute to collect ourselves and calm down. When we actively transition our thoughts into the right hemisphere and focus on the positives, we reconfigure the way in which we process.

By simply taking responsibility for the energy we bring into a given situation, we are projecting a certain version

14   "World Stroke Day Featuring Dr. Jill Bolte Taylor And Claudia Mason". 2020. *Facebook Watch.* https://www.facebook.com/shareyourstrokeofgenius/videos/530693587717508/.

of ourselves to others. I have found that oftentimes, when it comes to stroke survivors, friends and family don't know how to respond to the fact that a person they know has experienced such trauma. This is precisely why we have an obligation to take responsibility for the energy we bring. In a Stroke of Genius conversation with supermodel and stroke survivor Claudia Mason, she said that when people visit stroke survivors and don't know how to process what happened, we have to figure out how to share the energy. Do I as a stroke survivor come into your space or do you come into mine? "And all of a sudden, you are co-creating a moment," says Dr. Jill Bolte Taylor. "We become who we are in the present moment," she says.[15] When you really think about it, the only moment we ever have is the present one. If we are aware of ourselves and our thought process, and change our actions and the way that we interact with others, the world around us changes because now not only am I accepting myself, but I can love you more too. Ultimately, this is not just about you or me. It's bigger than that. We have the choice to walk into a room confidently and with a positive attitude, or we can let our anxiety get the best of us. It's our call. All of these series of moments and choices add up to create the person we are.

Another thing I've learned from this experience is that tomorrow is not a guarantee. Almost dying has shifted my perspective on the fragility of life. We can't take for granted every day we wake up because it's not a sure thing that we

---

15   "World Stroke Day Featuring Dr. Jill Bolte Taylor And Claudia Mason". 2020. *Facebook Watch*. https://www.facebook.com/shareyourstrokeofgenius/videos/530693587717508/.

will. The fact that we do awaken on any given day is a tre-mendous blessing. Not everyone does.

I aspire to live my life with a sense of urgency. But we are messy, and life is messy, so why do we even try? We should love ourselves for all that we are because, like Dr. Jill Bolte Taylor says, "We are beautiful life force powers of the universe."[16] We have so much to offer and our actions determine our quality of life. We may not always have control over what happens to us, but we always have control over how we respond.

When I was walking down the hallways of Kessler inpatient with my brother and my quad cane, I felt like all hope was lost. I was so far away from where I wanted to be mobili-ty-wise. But then I stopped, took a second to collect myself and reframed my thoughts. Instead, I told myself that things could be so much worse. I was fortunate to be alive and well and working toward recovery. No one said it would be easy, and it sure as hell wasn't. But I owed it to myself and to everyone else to give it my all. So, in that moment, I changed my perspective and came into my own as a positive life force power of the universe. I reframed my perspective for the better.

---

16   "World Stroke Day Featuring Dr. Jill Bolte Taylor And Claudia Mason". 2020. *Facebook Watch*. https://www.facebook.com/shar-eyourstrokeofgenius/videos/530693587717508/.

CHAPTER 13

A NEW COMPETITIVE ADVANTAGE

———

Ella Sofia, a fellow stroke survivor and habit coach, is constantly asking, "How can I turn a bad experience into a competitive advantage?" I think about this question a lot since my stroke. *How can I turn this traumatic situation into my very own competitive advantage, or the greatest thing that ever happened to me?*

"It becomes a habit, the effort that you put in," Ella told me.[17] As a habit coach in Edmonton Canada, Ella supports others who have gone through a traumatic experience like a stroke and helps them build effective and lasting habits for a more fulfilling life.

"When I first started, I was just blogging and sharing my tips and things that I've learned. Then I started doing a lot of reading on habit and neuroplasticity and how the brain changes, to see what else that sort of mindset could give to

---

17   Ella Sofia, phone conversation with author, 23 July 2019.

me, so that I could then provide value to other people," Ella shares.[18]

Perhaps somewhat surprisingly, Ella told me that the biggest change she experienced in her recovery was the shift in mindset on what it meant to be fully recovered. "So originally, for the first nine to ten years after my stroke ... the doctors would ask, do you feel like 98 percent? And I would always respond with yeah, a 98, or 99 percent. But I'm never going to be 100 percent again," she says.[19]

"But what I was doing was essentially telling myself that there's a part of me, like one or two percent, that I'm never going to get back. And, although that's true, I'm never going to be the same person again. It wasn't right for me to think I shouldn't strive to be that person again, even though things change ... so I tell people now that I am 100 percent because I'm doing my best. And that has been the most life changing thing," Ella admits.[20] And I thought *wow, how inspirational.* Look at this girl and how she turned her whole recovery around by simply shifting her frame of thought.

What if I worked to foster this same mindset about my own journey with recovery? What if, instead of focusing on what I could no longer do, I focused on what I *could* do. I am thankful for so many things—primarily, the gift of life and the simple things, like the fact that I can now walk without assistance, or that I can still see out of my eyes. When put

---

18   Ella Sofia, phone conversation with author, 23 July 2019.

19   Ella Sofia, phone conversation with author, 23 July 2019.

20   Ella Sofia, phone conversation with author, 23 July 2019.

this way, I realized that I had no reason at all to
or angry. I didn't make the choice to suffer a neai
experience, but I could make the choice in how I was ̧
to deal with it.

When I first started to ease back into working two years after
my stroke, I took an Uber one afternoon to my part-time job.
I started chatting with the driver, a sweet man from Jamaica.
He told me one of the more poignant things I've ever heard
that deeply resonated with me then and still does to this day.
After discussing my journey to recovery with him, he said
to me that I would be fine because, "God gives his toughest
soldiers the hardest battles."

I wasn't planning to get terribly religious in this book, but
I would be remiss not to mention how much of a role my
faith and attitude has played in my recovery. Everyone faces
hardships in life, and mine just happened to come in the
form of a paralyzing brain hemorrhage. It wasn't my first
life obstacle, and it certainly won't be my last. But right now,
this is my battle that I have to face. I see no point in getting
caught up in the technicalities of what I can no longer do
because I am a different person now. This is my reality, and
dwelling on what is gone is pointless. The question I have to
deal with is *how can I use this experience to my advantage
and help others with what I've learned?*

I feel it is my moral obligation and duty to find a way to see
the positives of this traumatic experience and help others
to do the same. If I could be like Ella Sofia and change my
definition of what it means to be fully recovered, I could
unlock a whole new realm of possibility. The limit to recovery

does not exist, and my journey toward recovery is however I decide to look at it.

This is why I ultimately decided to title this book *Fast Fwd: The Fully Recovered Mindset*. Things initially looked grim when I suffered a stroke, but #fastfwd almost three years and look what I'm doing now. Even since that day with the Jamaican Uber driver, I have made massive strides. Almost three years poststroke, and I have transitioned into a full-time job, traveled and commuted on my own, and walked in heels at a friend's wedding. I would say here that the sky's the limit, but quite honestly *there is no limit* to what we can achieve. Onward!

CHAPTER 14

"FEAR IS A MOTHERFUCKER"

———

"Some of the things that you're going through take longer to overcome and find solutions to than others, so you've got to have a certain level of patience and determination."[21] You may have heard of Alonzo Mourning and recognize him to be the NBA Hall of Famer who made a career out of playing center for the Miami Heat. I know him as an incredibly strong and inspiring man who suffered a serious kidney disease. Yet he still managed to turn this unfortunate obstacle into a tremendous opportunity to learn about himself and what he was capable of in terms of his recovery, eventually returning to play for the Heat after his kidney disease. An author himself, Alonzo Mourning has written about his professional career and personal experience in bouncing back from kidney disease and returning to basketball. He is an amazing person, and speaking with him only solidified for me the fact that I was talking with someone truly special who had an incredible perspective on life that I wanted to soak up.

———

21 Alonzo Mourning, conversation with author, 1 August 2019.

According to Alonzo Mourning, when it comes to your health and recovering from trauma, "You can't just wait for [the doctors] to tell you what you need to hear. You gotta go out and educate yourself on whatever you want to know."[22]

I learned firsthand how important it is to take your health into your own hands and make it a priority to understand what is going on and not just accept one doctor's opinion as law. When I was considering brain surgery, I visited countless brain surgeons to get their opinion on what should be done with my AVM. Some of the doctors told me that my AVM was too big and that they didn't think it was safe to operate on. Others told me I needed to remove this ticking time bomb ASAP because there was only an increased risk of a brain bleed with the passage of time. So, lots of conflicting opinions. That doesn't help when you're trying to make a decision as serious and life altering as brain surgery. While ultimately, my emergency brain surgery caused me problems of paralysis, vision loss, and cognitive fatigue, it didn't kill me. "What doesn't kill you makes you stronger, especially if you take the approach of overcoming," Alonzo Mourning told me.[23]

I had my Stroke of Genius when I was still at inpatient sub-acute rehab, and my perspective completely changed. It hit

22   Alonzo Mourning, conversation with author, 1 August 2019.

23   Alonzo Mourning, conversation with author, 1 August 2019.

me, and I realized just how lucky I was to still be on this earth. Sometimes when things get tough, I pause and think, holy s***! I almost died. In the beginning we weren't sure how much I would be able to recover, and I am so happy now that I have invested the time and effort in myself and in my recovery journey to get where I am today. Obviously not all days are easy. In fact, some days are quite difficult. But everyone has difficult days. No one is completely devoid of hardship. Our attitude in how we tackle each waking moment adds up to make the difference and mold us into the people we are today.

"I feel like God has placed enough resources around me, that it's up to me to go out and try to figure out what's the best approach for me to take because what I went through didn't kill me. It made me become a student of what I was told … and I felt like I'd be doing God a disservice [to not try my best]," Alonzo Mourning told me.[24] Like Alonzo Mourning, I feel that God has been present in my life and especially in this critical moment of need. I had the choice to turn away from God and deal with this on my own or strengthen my faith and rely on His love and goodness to help me through a trying time. And I chose the latter.

———————

Joe Borges, fellow stroke survivor, friend, and co-host of the brain injury podcast *The NeuroNerds,* understands how important a positive mindset is for recovery. "I believe in the power of prayer, energy, thoughts, whatever you want to

24   Alonzo Mourning, conversation with author, 1 August 2019.

call it because so many people from so many different back-grounds around the world were praying for me and sending me all this positive beautiful energy, and I'm here now, as functional as I've ever been, as positive as I've ever been, even though I shouldn't be," Joe said in a podcast episode on positive thinking.[25] Positivity has the power to literally transform lives. So, why does it sometimes seem so hard to embrace this mindset in daily life?

What sometimes holds us back from being happy and positive is fear. No reasons exist as to why we can't be happy; happiness is a choice. Are we just too scared to go all-in on positivity?

"Fear is a motherfucker," Joe eloquently states.[26] Fear holds us back from being the best version of ourselves. Imagine how amazing our world would be if we were not held back by the fear of failing and always embraced positivity. "I fight fear, and I fight reverting back to the old ways every single day. It's hard because thirty-plus years the same way, that's comfort to me," he says.[27]

But Joe also knows that having a positive mindset and outlook on his recovery, as well as a strong drive to break out of his comfort zone and set a new standard, will get him to

---

25   2020. *Theneuronerds.com.* https://www.theneuronerds.com/episodes/ep-92.

26   2020. *Theneuronerds.com.* https://www.theneuronerds.com/episodes/ep-92.

27   2020. *Theneuronerds.Com.* https://www.theneuronerds.com/episodes/ep-92.

where he wants to be. And I know that for me, the same is true. So, here's to embracing positivity and practicing gratitude in our daily lives.

CHAPTER 15

TRUST IN THE LORD WITH ALL YOUR HEART— PROVERBS 3:5

———

I grew up in a Catholic household and was raised to always go to church on Sunday and pray for those who are suffering. When I got to college, I wasn't as good about remembering to go to church. But I still had my faith, I still prayed, and I tried to live my life following Jesus' example.

After suffering a stroke, my faith strengthened. Here I was at a crossroads after my injury and I had to make a choice. I could look at what happened to me as a challenge and question God about why He would let something like this happen to me. Or I could choose to see it as a blessing. Perhaps the stroke brought me closer to God and strengthened my relationship with Him. Or maybe the devout friends from childhood, who I was reunited with as a consequence of my stroke, helped to strengthen me. Who knows, had I not suffered a near-death experience, maybe I would never have found it within myself to focus on my relationship with God and use a positive attitude to my advantage in recovery. I'm not saying this wouldn't have happened, but I do think this experience of trauma reaffirmed my belief and brought me closer to God.

Understanding and acknowledging the fact that I could have died gives my life new meaning. In essence, I was given a second chance to do things right. What that means, I still don't quite know, but I'm open to finding out. Now that I have had almost three years to reflect on my traumatic experience, I feel that I am in a good place and able to use my experience to help others and hopefully shed light on the journey. I aspire to empower and inspire others who might also be suffering a tough time.

My Jamaican Uber driver was right; God does give His strongest soldiers the toughest battles, and I'm willing to rise to the challenge of my own tough battle.

"We are all here to serve and to make a difference," Alonzo Mourning shared with me. "So, you just got to have a certain level of patience and determination."[28] Patience and determination is exactly what I strive for. It's not always easy, but no one said it was going to be. These battles are tough for a reason, and our ability to rise to the occasion when faced with hardship speaks volumes about our character and our drive.

---

28   Alonzo Mourning, conversation with author, 1 August 2019.

Waking up from my funk in the ICU and hearing about all the prayers that had been said for me was overwhelming. My parish community at Saint Patrick Church gathered to pray for me. Families and kids that I hadn't seen in years as well as people I didn't even know were all praying for *me*. Random people approached friends of my family to ask for updates on my recovery. While I was in the ICU, my parents decided to start sharing updates on a Caring Bridge page. Soon members of the Oak Knoll (my high school), Delbarton (my brother's high school), and Saint Patrick School communities were cooking meals for my family and taking care of my dog. I am so blessed. I thank God every day for blessing me with such an amazing support system.

CHAPTER 16

BIG GIRLS DON'T CRY (OR AT LEAST THIS ONE DOESN'T)

———

I don't cry. Since I had my stroke, I can count on one hand the number of times I've shed a tear. I'm not exactly sure why that is, but I realize that part of it may be because I'm no longer as openly emotional as I was before.

* * *

I'm an actor and a singer. For much of my life before my stroke, I juggled voice lessons, choir, the school musical, what have you. I loved it. Singing has been a huge part of my life. Whether it be in a formal group or just singing in the shower, singing has always been an outlet for me to express myself.

After my stroke (or should I say because of it), I lost my voice. My speaking voice. It almost sounded as if I were whispering whenever I tried to talk. I had no vocal inflection whatso-ever. My voice was completely monotone. So, not only did

I struggle my way through a rigorous physical and occupational therapy program, but speech and cognitive therapy as well.

While my speaking and vocal inflection has improved tremendously since May 2017, there's still a lot of improvement to be made. My family likes to joke and ask me, "Is anyone home?" because of my lack of response and outward display of emotion when asked something. And I try to show feeling, I really do.

I realized I had an issue with my expression when my friend Hannah told me she was getting married. I could be talking with her and be genuinely excited about something she said but not appear to be moved whatsoever. And no one wants to share exciting news like, *I got engaged!* to a deadpan face. So, I realized I needed to work on my expression.

To do so, I got serious with my cognitive therapy. My lack of expression was due to my facial paralysis, which I suffered due to my stroke. It was kind of like Bell's Palsy. I couldn't move the muscles on the left side of my face. Weird, I know. My smile was completely lopsided because the right side of my face would smile, but the left was paralyzed. So, in therapy, I retrained my smile. I hated the number of times my therapists had me smile and pucker, but it helped. The more I actively engaged my face muscles, the stronger and more even they became.

But even as my expression improved, I still wasn't crying. My family had a hard time telling how I was feeling because the way I physically presented myself didn't always align with how I felt. My dog died after my stroke, and although I was heartbroken, I didn't even cry for that.

Sometimes, my friends and family think I'm mad at them when I'm not, but because I tend to respond to any question or comment in a monotone, it often appears that way. I know many other stroke survivors who have become more emotional, crying more frequently after their injury, but I'm not one of them. In fact, I'm way less emotional than I was before.

As for my voice, it is a lot less monotone now. Unfortunately, my singing voice was affected, and that is something I hope to work on down the road. The doctors think my inability to match pitch stems from tightness in my vocal cords. My hope is that a voice therapist will be able to help me.

I do still have times when I get upset or frustrated by my lack of progress (or at least lack of as much progress as I want as quickly as I want it), but when I take a second to collect myself and reframe my perspective, I always feel better. I know I can't compare myself to anyone else because all of our journeys are different, and we all are on our own paths. My path happens to involve a struggle with physical limitations. But it could be anything, right? A toxic relationship, a challenging semester at college, anything at all. We are never going to be devoid of hardship in life. So, how are we going to respond to it?

* * *

According to one study by UCLA's Mindfulness Awareness Research Center, "regularly expressing gratitude literally changes the molecular structure of the brain, keeps the gray matter functioning, and makes us healthier and happier."29 *I'll say.* Shifting my attitude to regularly practice gratitude has been one of the more positive changes I've made in my life since my stroke. When I realized how much attitude contributes to success in recovery, I started to implement new habits to remind myself to be grateful.

Every morning when I wake up, the very first thing I tell myself is: Today is a beautiful day to be alive. Starting my morning with affirmations like this puts me in the right mindset to go forward and seize the day. It's all about perspective. How you view your life has a direct impact on the quality of your life.

When I was inpatient at Kessler, I made one of my best friends. Shadee, or as I call him, Duke, is the strongest person I know, having suffered a severe spinal cord injury that left him completely paralyzed. Although he is reliant on others for everything from bathing to eating, he has the best attitude of anyone I've ever met. I admire his strength, resilience, and perseverance. He refuses to give up and keeps working hard to improve. I draw much of my strength from him, and I am constantly inspired by his journey.

Back when I was inpatient, my mom and I would take breaks from therapy to sit outside and get some fresh air. On one such day, my mom approached a man in a wheelchair she had seen outside enjoying the sun for the past few days. They

---

29 "UCLA Mindful Awareness Research Center, Los Angeles, CA". 2020. *Uclahealth.Org.* https://www.uclahealth.org/marc/default.cfm.

chatted and the next day my mom wheeled me out to meet him. It was an instant connection; we hit it off and the rest is history.

What impressed me the most about Duke was his positivity. When you are confined to a wheelchair, unable to even stand up or move any of your limbs, it's very easy to slip into negative thoughts and question what the point of all this really is. *If you can't move or do anything on your own, what do you have to live for?* Duke showed me the answer to this question: *There is always so much to live for.* Maybe we lack mobility, but that doesn't mean we should lack a positive mindset and a willingness to persevere.

Practicing gratitude and finding opportunities to be thankful and appreciative has done wonders for me in recovery and in daily life. Taking a second in the middle of the day to pause and call to mind things I have to be grateful for immediately alters my mood for the better.

CHAPTER 17

POSITIVITY, AND ALL THAT JAZZ

———

My friendship with Duke only continued to grow while we were inpatient at Kessler. I hated rehab, but hanging out with Duke became the part of my day I most looked forward to. He always brightened up my day and put a smile on my face.

Duke suffered a complete spinal cord injury after being shot in the neck back in April of 2017. While I hate that this happened to him, I'm grateful that our shared experience with injury brought us together.

I often think, had I not suffered a stroke when I did, I never would have met Duke. He's been such a big part of my life—an amazing friend and big brother, as well as a constant motivation and cheerleader. We lift each other up and encourage each other to keep moving forward.

At inpatient, I followed a strict therapy schedule. Physical therapy from 8:00 a.m. until 9:30 a.m., occupational therapy from 1:00 p.m. until 2:30 p.m., and speech therapy from 3:30

p.m. until 4:45 p.m. In between these sessions, I would nap (more like pass out). Intensively exercising my brain was a huge cognitive strain for me in the early days poststroke, and while I may not have been fatigued physically, I quickly found that I needed to rest from the effort of retraining my brain.

* * *

One day in the middle of my speech therapy session, I got a knock on my door. Duke rolls in and declares, "I want you to meet my friend. I told him all about you and think you both would like each other. He's here already, and he's waiting right outside."

I was in the middle of my face exercises—a copious amount of repetitions of tongue twisters meant to engage my face muscles to work in synchrony. I still had at least three more rounds of "ba, beh, bee, bo, boo" to repeat before the session ended, but I told Duke to bring his friend in. I wanted to say hello.

Into my room comes none other than Ben Vereen, the dancer, singer, and actor made famous for his role as Chicken George in the popular 1977 historical miniseries, *Roots,* and role as O'Connor Flood in *All That Jazz.* I didn't recognize him at first, but my mom told me after who he was, and I recalled watching a portion of *Roots* in school as a child.

Ben has also had a remarkable journey with recovery, rehabilitating to the point that he can dance, sing, and act again. *But how is this possible?* I wondered.

The answer, once again, is through constant gratitude. "In order to keep that ongoing life force, we must continue to grow within ourselves toward a higher ground, which we are seeking," Ben told me.[30] Focusing on ourselves and our personal development is the greatest investment we can make.

Ben did just that. He spent a lot of time focusing on his recovery so he could get back to entertaining. He told me that when he was in therapy for the first time, his therapist asked him to reach and pick something up, to which he responded, *I can't*. "That's the first thing I want you to do," his therapist told him.[31] "Eliminate the word can't. We cannot afford the luxury of a negative thought."[32]

We cannot afford the luxury of a negative thought. When I think of all the times I've been negative when I could have been positive, it's astonishing. "That's the wonderful thing about the body, and the spirit within the body. We continue to always improve on ourselves," Ben told me.[33]

A little over two years after I met him, Ben called me to catch up. He asked how my recovery was coming along, and I told him I was trying to use my hand as much as I could. "You are not trying anything," he said. "You are either doing or you're not doing."[34]

---

30 Ben Vereen, conversation with author, 8 December 2019.

31 Ben Vereen, conversation with author, 8 December 2019.

32 Ben Vereen, conversation with author, 8 December 2019.

33 Ben Vereen, conversation with author, 8 December 2019.

34 Ben Vereen, conversation with author, 8 December 2019.

His response caught me off guard, and it took me a few minutes to digest the wisdom he had just imparted. I liked what he said, and ultimately it is true; we are either doing or we are not doing.

So, I no longer say I am trying to use my hand. I *am* using my hand.

PART 4:

GOAL SETTING

CHAPTER 18

GOALS, GOALS, AND MORE GOALS!

———

"I like to set goals. What about you?" my new physical therapist, Todd, asked me on my first day of outpatient physical therapy in July of 2017.

"Yes!" I exclaimed. It was my first day, and I was eager to impress Todd with my motivation and drive to succeed. I was ready to work hard and make improvements, getting back to activities I enjoyed. At this point in my journey, I could walk with a straight cane and the assistance of someone else since my balance was far from perfect. But I was motivated by an intense desire to ditch the cane and walk without any help. I wanted desperately to be "normal," and knew that the only way I would get there was by setting these short- and long-term goals and then putting in the work to achieve them.

I had a doctor's appointment with my neurosurgeon the following month, and I told Todd I really wanted to walk into his office without a cane. An ambitious goal, I know, but I thought I had the drive to achieve it. And Todd was all onboard.

To get to a point where I could walk without a cane, I had to get more comfortable walking on my own. This meant a lot of exercises geared toward improving my balance and narrowing my base of support, which may sound like nothing, but it is harder than you might imagine.

The most challenging thing for me during my time in outpatient physical therapy was undoubtedly learning how to weight shift onto my left side while walking. I had learned to compensate by rapidly relieving my left leg of any weight and hanging out on my right side.

Even after Todd cleared me for walking without the cane (just in time for my neurosurgeon appointment!), I still struggled with equal weight distribution while walking. My left side just didn't want to accept any weight.

It wasn't until I journeyed down to Birmingham, Alabama, for the first time in March of 2019 for a two-week, intensive bout of physical therapy, that it finally started to click. My physical therapist for the duration of the program, Danna Kay King, crafted a list of exercises for me that specifically targeted my left leg, ankle, and hip. For the first time, it all started to make sense. I understood what Todd had been saying all that time about shifting over to the left.

Maybe it was all those weight shifting exercises. Maybe it was the knee hyperextension control activities or ankle strengthening, or my improved sensation. Or maybe it was a little bit of everything. Either way, I not only improved my weight shifting and gait, but my left side awareness as well.

While my advancements in weight shifting and ankle mobility were subtle improvements, they had dramatic implications for my gait. I wouldn't say I walk "normally," considering I still have a slight limp and foot drop, but honestly speaking, if that's the best it gets, I'm totally satisfied. Like I've said, recovery is a mindset. Heck, everything in life could be considered a mindset. Instead of focusing on what we can't do, we have the incredible opportunity to be thankful for and appreciate all the things we *can* do. Obstacles are opportunities, and each one of us has the chance in every moment of the day to view our challenges as blessings or hardships. We get to decide how we invent our lives.

CHAPTER 19

LOOK MA, TWO HANDS!

———

When I began my outpatient therapy in July of 2017, my therapists had me set goals for the daily life activities I wanted to be able to do on my own. At first my goals were broad, big milestones: walk unassisted and without a cane, straighten my elbow, lift my wrist. As I crossed these huge milestones off my list, it became harder to narrow in on achievable goals. I wanted to use my hand, but arm progress was significantly slower and the advancements I did make were more nuanced and difficult to notice than the rapid progress I made with my leg. Walking independently and without a cane was a huge goal, but after this goal was achieved, I found it harder to realize the subtle improvements in my gait.

Pretty early on, I was able to move my arm, but I couldn't use it to assist with any functional activities. My occupational therapist asked me what kinds of goals I had for myself, and I told him it was really important to me to be able to fix my hair on my own. I had been getting by thus far with essentially one arm, my unaffected right. My left arm was just a deadweight that hung limp at my side. I couldn't use it, but I wanted to change that.

I knew that fixing a ponytail was an ambitious goal, but I really wanted to be able to do it. But how could I possibly do a ponytail with one hand? Using my left was just out of the question. There was no way my left hand could assist when I couldn't even hold a hair tie in my hand or consistently open my fingers.

Because my left hand was essentially useless, I found creative ways to accomplish tasks with one hand. I washed, and still wash, my hair with one hand because if I try to use my left to help, my fingers get caught in my hair and I have trouble untangling them. The tone in my hand overpowers most actions I voluntarily initiate. When I try to reach for an object, my hand often clenches into a fist, making it impossible for me to open my fingers.

This was a rough adjustment. Whose fingers don't listen to them? It's so frustrating. When I tell my hand to open, it does the opposite. The connection from my brain to the nerves in my hand was severed, therefore, the proper signal could not travel successfully down to my hand. This meant I had to relearn new ways to establish those neural pathways in my brain that would signal my hand to move.

––––––––––

It wasn't until I completed a three-week intensive constraint-induced movement therapy program for my left arm at the University of Alabama at Birmingham in June of 2019 that I really began to see functional progress with my hand. At the Taub Clinic at UAB, stroke patients work one-on-one with a therapist for four hours a day for the duration of the program. On top of that, after each four-hour session, patients return to their hotel rooms to continue using their affected upper extremity.

Intense would be an understatement. It was *the* most aggressive form of rehab out there. But it worked. At UAB, everything I wanted to do would have to be with my left hand. Difficult and incredibly frustrating, yes, but a necessary step to create the habit of use.

Researchers at the Taub Clinic found that after a stroke causing hemiparesis, or paralysis of one side, patients quickly developed the habit of learned disuse. The research showed that in as little as four days, the brain can learn to reshape itself, either positively or negative.[35] What this meant for me is that my brain had learned to ignore my whole left side, almost as if it weren't even there.

* * *

Our brains are smart. If that affected side isn't being used, our brains will adjust to nonuse. Why waste the valuable brain space on something that won't work the way you want it to?

According to Dr. Taub himself, the scientist who developed CI therapy, there's a fierce competition in the brain to allocate resources, and my brain figured it was better to utilize that space for other things.[36] "The brain responds to increased use," he told me. "The brain contains a map, a sensory map

35   Mary Bowman, conversation with author, 12 June 2019).

36   Dr. Edward Taub, conversation with author, 27 June 2019.

and a motor map of portions of the body, and the size of this cortical representation of body parts is directly related to how much we use that body part," he told me.[37]

This neural excitability is key in recovery. My main takeaway from my time at UAB was that the more I engaged my hand, the better. That is why, when I opted to write this book, I decided I would type my manuscript with two hands. I wrote my first book through a combination of voice dictation and one-handed typing, but for this book I made an effort to type with two hands.

These days, typing with two hands is not nearly as quick or fluid as it was before. In fact, since for the most part my fingers don't cooperate enough to perform isolated motions on a keyboard, I use an adapted stylus. Just think: it takes a considerable amount of coordination, control, and exactitude to press a computer key. Since I couldn't effectively control my fingers (yet), my therapist at UAB cut an angled hole in a piece of foam and stuck a stylus in it. I could hold the foam in my hand and peck at the keys with the stylus. Much simpler and more efficient than trying to actually use my fingers.

At the time of this writing, six months after my trip down to Birmingham to rehabilitate my arm and hand, I am using my left side more to engage in activities like zipping my coat, and tying my shoes. That's right, I can now do what at one point seemed impossible—I can tie my own shoes!

---

37   Dr. Edward Taub, conversation with author, 27 June 2019.

Now, I can also successfully put my hair in a bun using both hands. I'm a little slower than I used to be, but the important thing is that I'm actually doing it. Fixing a ponytail is much more difficult, and progress is slow, but onward!

CHAPTER 20

NOT JUST A PIPE DREAM

———

"Maddi, can you find the vertical asymptote of this rational function?" my high school precalculus teacher, Mr. Moloughney, asked me during class. "Sure," I halfheartedly replied. Math was never my strong suit, and I tended to gravitate more toward the humanities and languages in my academic pursuits. I could do math. I just needed someone to explain a mathematical concept multiple times before it clicked in my mind.

Mr. Moloughney was very patient with me. In fact, it got to a point where he would be teaching the class how to find the inverse of a function but single me out by asking, "Maddi, do you have any questions?" And let me tell you, probably much to his chagrin, I always had a lot of questions. But I needed to make sure I properly understood. Some concepts just took a little bit longer to click in my mind.

* * *

In April of 2019, I hit a major recovery milestone. I started working full time. I began my first ever full-time job as a reinsurance junior underwriting associate. I felt that by this point I had reached a level in my recovery where I was ready to dedicate time to focus on other important things besides my physical recovery. This job was the perfect opportunity for me to test my limits and learn something new.

Now that I've been working for a full year, I can say I truly enjoy the work that I do and I'm grateful for the chance to learn under the tutelage of such intelligent colleagues who are invested in my personal development. I know I'm not going to learn everything in one day, one month, or even in one year, and I am very appreciative of everyone who has helped me so far in my learning process.

To think that right after my stroke I couldn't remotely conceptualize the idea of working at a full-time job, to diving in head first and just doing it, is absolutely crazy. Finally, I was participating in the work-life grind like everyone else. It felt like a badge of honor.

* * *

All my life, I took any job or internship opportunity I had for granted. It was just a vehicle for me to make money and gain experience. Maybe I liked it, maybe I didn't, but whatever. At least I was making money to spend on what I really wanted to do. Working was just something everyone had to do to pay the bills.

While this may be true, my perspective on work has changed. I am so grateful for the chance to contribute and add value to an organization that cares for me. I think back to when I was still in a wheelchair, unable to move my neck, walk, or remember like I used to. Who would have thought that that girl would be working?

My life—my mobility and mental capacities—is an insane gift. I realized I had this unique opportunity through work to push my limits and prove to myself and everyone what I was capable of. Having a stroke caused me to reframe my perspective to be more appreciative of the little things. I have legs that work. I have my mind. Heck, I still have the ability to understand and communicate in English *and* Spanish. A stroke can affect people in a number of ways, and I felt like I had the best possible outcome of a sucky situation. I had my mind and I had my language. How fortunate was I? Because of that, I was able to work full time at a company where I could use my language skills and exercise myself cognitively on a daily basis with challenging work.

When I first started, I was absolutely shattered after an eight-hour day. But as I adjusted and things in the office got busier, I found myself needing to take fewer breaks and able to work longer hours. The busy season for underwriters is the months leading up to January, and I surprised myself by being able to work longer hours to support the team. All along, my goal had been to get back to activities I enjoy and be "normal." And I was doing it; I was working, which is about as "normal" as you can get.

I had a better understanding now of all my friends who groaned about their exhaustion after a tough work week. Pre-stroke Maddi would have done the same. But I had a fresh perspective and new way of viewing things. Sure, I'm probably more exhausted after a long day of work than pre-stroke Maddi, but the difference is now I'm actually appreciative of that feeling of exhaustion.

When I get really tired, I take a second to stop and remind myself of how far I've come. *Remember when you couldn't move at all, and the idea of managing full-time work seemed like an unachievable pipe dream?* Well, *I* certainly do.

CHAPTER 21

IT'S ONLY ONE STEP, BUT IT'S A BIG ONE

———

"Let me know what train you take in, then from Penn Station it's just a few quick stops on the A and a couple blocks' walk," my friend texted me. Which, theoretically speaking, should be no problem. But in case you forgot, I had a brain injury, and that makes everything way more complicated.

Many people who don't know me very well don't understand the scope of my problem with spatial awareness. Just from looking at me, one could see I have a limp or that occasionally my arm bends up when I'm walking, but my visual issues and problems with awareness are less easily detected.

Still, when I would receive texts like this one asking that I get myself to a friend's apartment, I would have to explain to them that this just wasn't possible and request that they meet me at the station. I hated having to do this, but fortunately I have nice friends who didn't mind meeting me halfway. For the most part, the people I socialized with during this time were aware of my capabilities and of what I could handle.

A big therapy goal of mine for the year 2019 was to be able to take the train by myself. I figured this would give me more freedom in my daily life, and I was all about increasing my independence. I could no longer drive because of my vision problems, so I was dependent on getting a ride. When my balance and visual scanning improved to the point that my parents were no longer terrified (okay, only slightly less terrified) of me knocking into people or falling over, I started taking Uber by myself to get to the gym or to work.

But I didn't want to stop there. Getting into an Uber on my own was great, but there was so much more I wanted to be able to do. Once I got out of the Uber, I had to be able to navigate my way to where I was going. Successfully accomplishing this task involved way more effort and planning than I thought.

* * *

When I started working full time in April of 2019, I ran into the issue of how I was going to get to work. I couldn't drive due to vision problems, and my parents worked as well, so I couldn't always count on them for rides. But spring was right around the corner, and I loved to walk, so I thought it might not be a bad idea to learn to commute myself.

There is a train station in my town that is a fifteen-minute walk from my house. I learned that I could walk to the train station, hop on the train, and get off one stop later, where a shuttle would pick up the morning commuters and drive them from the station to our campus.

This seemed like a deal too good to be true. Talk about a luxury commute, right? So, with the start of a new job, I set a new goal to be able to commute into work without help. To get there, I broke down my goal into smaller steps.

First, I had to practice walking to the station and get comfortable enough to do it on my own. At the time, my dad was in between jobs, so he was able to walk with me to the station every morning for practice.

Every work-day morning that spring and summer I got out of bed at 5:30 a.m., got dressed, packed my lunch, and headed out to the station with my dad. I was pleased that the more I practiced walking to the train station, the faster I got. Nowadays the walk only takes me fifteen minutes on my own, whereas in those first few weeks of working it took me around thirty.

Once we got to the station, my dad and I would wait to board the 8:01 westbound train to Dover. Riding the train from Chatham was a whole new dilemma because to board the train, I needed to manage a massive step up from the platform.

At first, my dad would stand behind me as I tried to manage the steps on my own and help me if I needed it. Luckily, there was a railing on the right side of the train that I was able to grab and use to help hoist my legs up. Challenging, yes, but it was a good strengthening exercise for me and I surprised my dad and even myself by my ability to do it.

We rode the train one stop (often not even needing to present a ticket to the conductor because it was so short of a journey) and disembarked at Madison. Once I got off the train, my next hurdle was navigating the crowds and walking down the stairs fast enough to make the shuttle.

When I got off the train, I booked it to the staircase. Well, "booked it" might be an overstatement since I had to safely navigate my way and remember to look around. The latent danger of running into a fellow commuter meant I had to constantly stay alert and remember to turn my head and check my left blind spot. By cultivating a better sense of awareness of my surroundings, I became more comfortable with traveling. Within a couple months' time, I was able to walk myself to the station and get to work on my own, with no assistance.

* * *

Over Halloween weekend in 2019, I hit yet another major recovery milestone. I took the subway by myself for the first time poststroke. Which may not seem like a huge deal, but trust me, it is. In retrospect, it is probably still not the safest thing for me to do, but I needed to prove to myself that it was possible. I wanted to show myself that I could get around without help.

* * *

After work on Friday, November 1, 2019, I packed my backpack for the weekend and hopped on the train to New York Penn. I was headed to the apartment of my college roommates for an evening of catching up. By this point, I had been taking the train a lot on my own, but navigating crowded situations with my vision loss was still a challenge.

It's very busy in Penn Station. No one is paying attention to what's in front of them, instead focused intently on their phone screens. This can be a messy situation for a person with visual and spatial awareness issues like me. Lots of potential for accidents.

While on the train, I decided that once I arrived, I would try to take the subway to Chelsea, since my friends' apartment was only one stop away and a two-block walk. But I knew that if I were to actually do this, I'd have to be hyperaware of things on my left side. I don't always pay attention and have been known to run into signs or people on my left side because I don't see them. But if I were to do the subway on my own, this simply could not happen.

So, when I got off the train, I headed over toward where the subway was and made my way to the E downtown line. I took my time walking and stopped to read the signs to make sure I was heading in the correct direction. There was no need to rush. I was extra careful, looking over my left side constantly. When my train arrived, I hopped on (thankfully it wasn't crowded) and hopped off one stop later.

Luckily, one of my other college roommates who was going to dinner happened to also have just gotten off the subway, and so we managed to meet up near the exit and walk over together (shoutout to Find my Friends for helping us locate each other).

The trickiest part of this little adventure was definitely making sure that I saw everything. Prior to having a stroke, I never thought about visual scanning, but I knew that if I were to be walking by myself in the train station, there was no room for error, and I had to be as careful as I could. So, I walked slowly and deliberately, taking my time to scan and read all the signs and make sure I wasn't headed toward collisions with passersby. I made sure I allowed myself ample time to navigate, so I was never in a rush. I needed to take my time.

I was so proud of myself for taking the subway all by myself, but I still don't quite feel 100 percent confident in my ability. I know I'm vulnerable with my walking and lack of awareness, so this is all still a work in progress for me. But they're all steps in the right direction, and I know I'm getting there slowly but surely.

Now, when a friend asks me to meet them at their apartment in the city, I feel more confident in my ability to get there on my own. It helps knowing that from the train station I can easily catch a cab or order an Uber if I need to. One thing I've just come to accept is that I now have more expenses than I used to. Traveling on public transport is harder now than it used to be, so I have to call an Uber more than the average person. Little things like this take some adjusting.

* * *

When navigating public transport, there's so much to be aware of. Because of my vision loss, I have to be extra aware with my other senses. I try to pay extra attention to the sounds I hear to warn me when someone is approaching. Cultivating a sense of awareness is much harder than I would have thought, but the more I practice it, the more it improves. I know the more I place myself in situations slightly outside of my comfort zone, while remaining safe of course, the better I will get. Stroke recovery is a lifelong process, and I'm committed to making continued progress.

CHAPTER 22

HEEL COMES THE BRIDE

It was only a hundred feet away, but it could have been a mile. I was so nervous and just wanted to make the short journey without incident. I started my walk and instantly felt the nerves kick in with four hundred pairs of eyes on me. The music began to play, and I proceeded to walk down the aisle.

When my childhood friend, Hannah, got engaged, she asked me to be her maid of honor, to which I humbly obliged. She was the first of any of my friends to get married, and I was so excited. I knew that as maid of honor I would have a lot of responsibilities, including the bachelorette and the bridal shower.

Soon after Hannah asked me to be a part of her wedding, I set a goal to walk down the aisle in heels for the big day. I knew it was an ambitious goal (especially considering I couldn't walk well without a leg brace), but I was determined to achieve this goal. Pre-stroke, I loved to rock a pair of platform heels for a big night out, and while I knew I wouldn't be able to do this for the wedding, I was hoping to at least get some satisfaction from wearing a pair of heels, no matter how short they were.

To achieve my goal of wearing heels for the wedding, I started practicing walking in an inch-high pair for fifteen minutes a day a few times a week while wearing my Bioness. A few months before the wedding, I invested in a Bioness unit, which is a leg cuff with an electrode that sends an electrical signal down to my ankle to trigger it to lift and facilitate a heel-toe strike. This would take the place of my leg brace.

As much as I liked (read: hated) having a leg brace, it wasn't the most attractive option, and I was limited in my footwear selection when I wore it. The brace didn't fit in all shoes, and tennis shoes tended to work best, as they typically had a slight lift in the heel. As much as I loved my trainers (especially considering the rise of streetwear and chunky platform sneakers, conveniently timed for my situation), I still dreamt of the day I could get back to heels, boots, and sandals. God, I missed the simple things in life, like a pair of flip-flops at the beach or tall warm boots in the cold winter months.

There were a lot of shoes I couldn't wear with my brace anymore, and even pants too. I actively sought out wide-leg pants that would fit over my brace or Bioness, concealing it from sight. Nice wide-leg pants were a little harder to come by, but I made do and slowly started to build up a collection.

* * *

What I loved most about walking with the Bioness was that it opened up a whole new world of shoes to me. Because the thing that lifted my ankle correctly to walk was a cuff I wore around my calf, I could wear whatever shoes I wanted, so long as they didn't get in the way of the electrical stimulation.

Amazing, right? I bet you can see where I'm going with this.

* * *

Which brings me back to the heels. I knew that with the Bioness, I'd be able to practice walking in heels and safely wear them for the wedding. As you can probably imagine, heels and a leg brace don't go well together. So, once I bought myself a Bioness (which was no small investment, unfortunately) I began walking around the house in heels a little bit a few times a week, and a little bit every day in the weeks leading up to the wedding. It was hard work, and I wasn't the fastest walker, but I was doing it nonetheless. A little bit of walking each day in heels and the Bioness was preparing me for the big day.

When the big day came, I was as ready as I could be. The quality of my walking wasn't as fluid as I wanted it to be, but I could walk. *I could walk,* and that in and of itself felt like a huge blessing.

The night before the wedding, I learned that I would be proceeding down the aisle alone. Although I was prepared to walk in heels down the aisle, this scared me and made me nervous because I had assumed I'd have the help of the best man. I wished someone could have been there just in case. But alas, we can't always get what we want.

After I walked down the aisle, I would have to walk up the big step to the altar and sit on the bride's left-hand side. One concern with this was that to walk up the step to the altar, I would need assistance because there was no railing for me to hold. I would also have my bouquet of flowers in hand.

I expressed my concerns to Father Bob, who graciously offered to take my arm and help me up to the altar. I was so relieved; even just that little bit of help getting me up to the altar would make me feel a lot more confident.

Once I was safely seated up at the altar, I was responsible for holding the bride's flowers as well as my own. I'm not going to lie. They got to be really heavy, but I kept telling myself that I only had to hold them for one hour and I couldn't drop them. Even though my affected hand lost its grip on the stems of the flowers, I sat there and continued holding them in my right. I needed to do this to show myself that I could. This was my major responsibility for the day, and I couldn't mess it up.

At the end of the ceremony, I walked out of the church on the arm of the best man, who supported me as I stepped down from the altar. He was standing to my left, so he grabbed my left arm to help me down. This typically makes me uneasy because it's my weaker and affected side. I feel more comfortable when being supported on my right side because my sensation is better. Although it was slow and labored, I surprised myself by being able to function leading with my left side.

After the pictures, everyone headed over to enjoy the reception, for which I changed into sneakers. I had achieved my goal of walking in heels for the ceremony, but I didn't want to risk injury for the reception and photos that would be taken outside. Uneven terrain outdoors can be tricky, and I feel more comfortable in my sneakers. Luckily, the bridesmaids' dresses were floor-length gowns.

After the pictures and at the reception, I surprised myself by dancing the night away. Well, *dancing* might be an overstatement. I wasn't much of a dancer before, but I was even less of one now. However, that didn't stop me from busting some moves on the dance floor. I think of it like therapy; this was just another opportunity to engage my left side. All in all, it was an incredible evening.

PART 5:

PUSH IT TO THE LIMIT

CHAPTER 23

LONDON CALLING

———

October of 2019 was a busy month for me because not only did I have the wedding but big international travel plans as well. The week after Hannah's wedding I headed to London for my first trip abroad since having a stroke. Independent travel was and still is a massive goal of mine, and this week would give me a good idea of where I stood in my progress toward this goal.

On October 11, 2019, my brother and I flew over to London for an eight-day holiday to visit our younger sister (who was studying a semester at Kings College), and my best friend from Georgetown. I would be spending the week at my friend Freddy's apartment in West London, and my brother would be staying with some coworkers who recently moved to the city.

I was so excited; I hadn't been back to Europe since I studied abroad in Madrid in 2015. So, this trip felt long overdue. But a part of me was also nervous for this adventure. I needed to prove to myself and to my family that I was capable of independence abroad. This trip would give me a good idea of what I could do on my own and what I still needed to work on.

My siblings and I had semi-planned out a bunch of fun activities for this week, including day trips to Dublin and Oxford, some nice dinners in London, and of course, some shopping. I was taking the whole week off from work, and my brother was working out of his company's London office for two days, so I figured this gave me some time to focus on my exercises and writing while he was at work and my sister was in class. Because I had already visited London once before, I didn't feel the pressure to cram in a million tourist activities while I was there. I was looking forward to just hanging out with my siblings and Freddy in a cool city.

Before my brother and I departed for London Heathrow, my mom told me to pay extra attention to my body and the signals it gave me of tiredness. Neuro fatigue hits me harder now, and when it does it hits me like a ton of bricks. I had to be extra aware of my body's signals so I didn't overexert myself.

I would definitely be going out for drinks with Freddy and my siblings, so I had to also keep in mind my limits when it came to alcohol. Alcohol affects me differently now, and while I still do enjoy social drinking with good friends, I can't handle as many drinks as I used to. When I have a couple of drinks in me now, the liquor negatively affects my walking and slurs my speech. I wear a brace and already have a slight limp, so I like to joke that my normal walking looks like I'm drunk. So, I can't *actually* get drunk since I'm already impaired.

When we went out to dinner, on multiple occasions the bouncer standing outside the bar stopped me and asked if I was okay to come into the restaurant. I suspect he thought I already had too much to drink. So, I found myself frequently struggling to explain my situation to the bouncers: I just look like I'm drunk even when I'm not because of the way I walk. This happened a few times over the course of the week and got to be a little annoying. But I understand the bouncers' point of view. Here comes a girl who can't walk well, trying to get into the bar. It took a lot out of me to remain patient and calmly explain myself.

After suffering a stroke, I also realized that my metabolism had changed. I couldn't just eat whatever I wanted anymore without consequence. I started to notice that I gained weight when I ate carb-heavy meals. So, for the past two years I'd been making an effort to restrict my diet to low carb. I essentially hadn't had a slice of pizza, a beer, or bread in two years. All this effort, and I was just maintaining (or sometimes gaining) weight. It was really annoying. The last thing I wanted was to come back from a week in London to discover I'd gained ten pounds. I was on holiday, yes, so I could loosen up my diet a bit and enjoy myself, but weight loss/maintenance was still important to me, so I couldn't go crazy.

London to Dublin to Oxford and back again to New Jersey, my excursion to Europe showed me that I am managing better than I thought. What real point was there in focusing on what I could no longer do? Instead, I thought it would be much more productive if I focused my efforts on the skills I did have and the goals I am working toward. For next time, I would like to have more confidence in managing my luggage alone and navigating crowded airports. This trip only further revealed to me the importance of a positive attitude in recovery.

CHAPTER 24

NOT JUST ANOTHER FAMILY BARBECUE

———

Thanks to social media, I now have a good friend from the Netherlands, Jeroen, who taught me the importance of seeking rehabilitation opportunities in the activities of everyday life. Jeroen organizes and hosts frequent barbecues for his family and friends because it's good cognitive and physical rehab. If barbecuing is something you enjoy, why not just go for it?

* * *

For me, I found alternative therapy through planning my friend's bachelorette party. As maid of honor in my friend Hannah's wedding, I had many obligations to fulfill, one of which was organizing the bachelorette party. It took me some time, but I took pride in the fact that I was able to successfully plan and execute the whole thing—from a lingerie gift exchange cocktail hour and a dinner at a neat hole-in-the wall Italian restaurant to a ghost walking tour and an evening of chocolate cocktails at Max Brenner. The whole event was a huge success, and just one example of how I tried to take my life into my own hands and turn my obligation to party plan into an opportunity for cognitive rehabilitation.

I knew going into it that planning a bachelorette party would really test my ability to plan and organize. But luckily that was something I had been working on.

After my stroke, I underwent a rigorous cognitive therapy program because I initially struggled with my memory, attention to detail, and ability to plan and execute. I used to have an incredible memory and be very detail-oriented, so I was anxious to get back to feeling like myself.

Cognitive therapy was annoying and challenging. I couldn't understand why I was having such trouble doing simple tasks like taking inventory of items in a closet, or planning out my activities for the next day. Not only did the neuro fatigue set in quickly, but I also found myself unable to concentrate on one thing for long periods of time.

One important lesson I've learned from this whole experience with recovery is that I need to allow ample time to plan out activities that I was once able to do on a whim. As much as I hated cognitive therapy, the therapists taught me something I still do to this day—write everything down. I record my to-do lists, daily journals, doctors' appointments, and notes in the Google Keep app and Google calendar. I initially started writing everything that happened down to refresh my memory so I wouldn't forget. At the end of every day, I would write down what I did. I thought it was so cool to be able to flip back through my past entries and really see just how far I've come.

***

A big part of recovery following a traumatic experience like stroke is working to get back to doing things that used to be enjoyable. For a while following my stroke, I didn't want to see people I knew because I was embarrassed by the fact that I couldn't move my left side at all or do things like I used to. An independent life was inconceivable to me. While I'm still working toward independence, doing things like planning a party give me more confidence that I'll be able to plan out even more activities and get one step closer to where I want to be.

In the early days of his rehab, Jeroen came to a realization very similar to my own: to get better and do the things he wanted to do again, he had to set ambitious goals and break them down into actionable steps. "I realized that I need these goals, these ridiculous goals to get me motivated," he shared.[38] From reaching a point where he could ride his electric bicycle to work, or planning and executing a successful family cookout, Jeroen has been not only working toward, but achieving these landmark accomplishments. It may not sound like a big deal to organize a family barbecue, but trust me, it's a massive deal. Strokes have a funny way of messing with your ability to plan, and that is an often-overlooked obstacle to recovery.

An important lesson I learned from my friend Jeroen was how crucial it is to constantly set goals for yourself to stay motivated. Perhaps more important than our physical ability

---

38   Jeroen Mars, conversation with author, 24 August 2019.

to achieve those goals is our mentality and drive to work toward them in small, actionable steps. "I draw a road map of where I want to go and what goals I want to achieve," Jeroen told me.[39] For example, as a form of cognitive therapy, Jeroen started planning and organizing BBQs, as a reason to get his family and friends together while practicing cooking and his executive functioning. And I must say, after seeing pictures from his barbecuing events, I'm on the hunt for the next opportunity to head over to the Netherlands and taste his short ribs or smoked fish myself. Such a delicious way to incorporate rehab with daily life skills!

Another friend I've made through my recovery, Dr. Hugh Snyder, is a family practice doctor in Summit, New Jersey, who also suffered a stroke and has made what I would consider to be a remarkable recovery. You probably won't be surprised to hear that it was in large part due to the ambitious goals he set himself and his crazy drive to achieve them. "My goal is to be able to say that I had a stroke, and I didn't miss a day of skiing. And I achieved it," he told me.[40]

Not only did he achieve the crazy goal of being able to ski again, but he also got back to doing something that happens to be one of my long-term personal goals—running. "I went [to the gym] every day, treading on the elliptical, then went in the pool and worked on my arm in the pool, and so on. I was

---

39   Jeroen Mars, conversation with author, 24 August 2019.

40   (Dr. Hugh Snyder, conversation with author, 22 June 2019).

on the treadmill, and I got up to three miles per hour, a brisk walk, that I would later convert into a run," Dr. Snyder said.[41]

"I kept trying all different things to reduce spasticity," he said. "I thought I could reduce the spasticity by fatiguing the muscles," he shared. But when that didn't work, Dr. Snyder refused to give up. He brought his goal to run to his physical therapist, and received some new advice on how to achieve it.

Guess what? He did it! The secret? "Metatarsal lifts," he shared.[42] Similar to me, Dr. Snyder has a decent amount of spasticity in his leg, which tightens the muscles and causes them to contract (especially when you least want them to, of course). I have the same problem, which is why I need to wear a leg brace or the Bioness. But Dr. Snyder told me the metatarsal lift fits in the sole of your shoe underneath the ball of your foot. He started out walking on the treadmill, and that walk progressed to a jog at two and a half miles per hour. "I almost started crying," he said. "I can't believe I finally achieved this goal."[43]

Wow. If I could reach a point where I could run, even if it looked like a chicken with his head cut off, I would be happy. I did try to run once poststroke in physical therapy, only to realize that it's way harder than it looks. I definitely underestimated how difficult it would be to make the transition from a brisk-paced walk to running. So, my running looked awkward and disjointed.

---

41   (Dr. Hugh Snyder, conversation with author, 22 June 2019).

42   (Dr. Hugh Snyder, conversation with author, 22 June 2019).

43   (Dr. Hugh Snyder, conversation with author, 22 June 2019).

While I only managed to run (well, "run" is a generous term for my flailing limbs) for a few seconds before I had to slow down from fatiguing muscles, the important thing is that I tried. I haven't attempted running in a while, as I've been more focused on regaining my confidence walking with the Bioness and strengthening my arm and leg, but running is still a huge goal of mine.

My 2020 vision from a physical therapy point of view is to run a mile. Ambitious, I know, and at the time of this writing (January 2020), I have not yet accomplished it, but I'm actively taking steps forward to achieve this goal in therapy and on my own time. Trust me, one way or another, by December of 2020 I will have run a mile. And I'll get to tell you all about it.

CHAPTER 25

RUN THE MILE YOU'RE ON

———

Recovery is a marathon, not a sprint, and we can't compare ourselves to the journeys of others. Every recovery experience is unique and different, so we've just got to run the mile we're on.

In February of 2019, I flew down to Miami with my dad. The purpose of this trip was to see my good friend, Greg Nance, complete the World Marathon challenge. Seven marathons, in seven days, on seven continents.

Yep, you read that right. Seven marathons, seven days, seven continents. It's the ultimate test of human endurance, and not to mention a logistical nightmare, with participants flying a total of 75,000 miles from continent to continent after running 26.2 miles in all kinds of weather and conditions. Lifetime elite air status, anyone?

Novo, Antarctica, --> Cape Town, Africa, -->Perth, Australia -->Dubai, Asia, -->Madrid, Europe -->Santiago, South America--->Miami, North America. That's wild stuff right there.

My dad and I were looking for an escape from the brutal New Jersey winter, and as I wasn't working at the time, we thought, why not head down to warm and sunny Miami for a week and catch Greg's race? Finishing one marathon, let alone the World Marathon Challenge, is no minor accomplishment. And I wanted to be there to see it.

The final race took place along the Miami boardwalk, and Greg was at pace to finish around 2:30 a.m. After a brief nap, my dad and I woke up to walk down to the finish line. Since I had the stroke, I had taken to wearing an Apple watch to track my daily step count. The way I see it, I am so grateful to be able to take steps and walk (without assistance now, too) that I feel I need to do it as often as I can. Which can get to be difficult now given my work schedule, but whenever I can, I make an effort to move as much as possible. The flashbacks to when I was confined to a wheelchair, unable to sit up on my own, motivate me each and every moment of the day to get stepping and exercising those muscles that I, at one point, wasn't sure if I'd ever regain control over again.

It's a weird situation, and people who don't know me tend to be surprised when I say that technically nothing is wrong with my muscles. The crux of my issue with hemiparesis is that the neural pathways in the brain that map out my motor planning don't work like they used to.

So, even though it was 1:00 a.m., I was ecstatic to get up, get moving, and cheer on Greg as he completed this amazing achievement. Because the runners were on a strict seven-day time line to complete the challenge, they were forced to run their marathons at any hour of the day, and rest and recover on the plane. The Miami leg of the race began the night of the sixth, and just happened to be finishing up around 2:00 the next morning.

Our walk over to the finish line was no small feat either because we needed to walk over a mile to reach the finish. Afterward, I almost felt like I had just run a marathon myself. So, as you can imagine, I was already well on my way to achieving my daily goal of ten thousand steps by 2:30 in the morning. Normally, walking over a mile would really tire me out and I'd need to take breaks, but not this morning. I was a woman on a mission, and I was going to see Greg finish this race no matter what it took.

While much of recovery lies in our attitude and approach to the recovery process, another contributing factor is our willingness to continuously push our limits. What once would have been second nature to me was now a challenge, and I was committed to testing my limits to see what I was capable of. I walked all the way to the finish line and then was able to rest for a bit there while waiting for Greg to finish his own incredible physical challenge.

Being there to support him for the end of an incredibly taxing seven days was a truly special experience. For someone who had just run a marathon in every continent on the world in the span of a week, he looked pretty good. I was expecting to be greeted by a run-down, haggard, exhausted runner, but that's not Greg Nance. Despite his overexerted body, he approached me after the race with a huge smile and massive bear hug. He had just completed a landmark achievement (for only the craziest of people), and so had I. I pushed myself to walk farther than I was accustomed to and surprised myself with my ability to do it.

The next morning, I met up with Greg for a post-race victory banquet at Five Guys. We then went on a fun walk around Miami to get the blood circulating. I was surprised he wanted to walk after all that running, but I wasn't complaining. Movement is always good. I ended that day with a record eighteen thousand steps.

For me, this trip to Miami was more than just an awesome excuse to catch up with and support Greg in his physical endeavors. I may have not run 183.5 miles in the span of seven days, but I too pushed my limits that week, walking an average of 12,470 steps a day. The way I see it, if Greg can do it, I certainly can too!

One of the reasons that Greg has been so successful in his running endeavors is because he understands the importance of pushing your limits and not comparing your journey to anyone else's. "It's all about mindset. You've just got to run the mile you're on," Greg says.[44]

We could all probably be a bit more like Greg Nance and focus on our own unique challenges without comparing them to the trials and tribulations of others. I firmly believe we are all on our own unique paths, facing our own obstacles. Maybe we aren't suffering dehydration or muscle cramping from running multiple marathons, and instead we are dealing with

---

44   "Run the Mile You're on: Greg Nance." 2019. *CJBS Insight.* https://insight.jbs.cam.ac.uk/2019/run-the-mile-youre-on-greg-nance/.

muscle weakness on our affected side poststroke. Maybe we have trouble managing fatigue and seizures, or we struggle to cope with debilitating migraines. Or maybe we're grappling with the challenges of weight loss or transitioning jobs.

It doesn't matter. We shouldn't compare our journey to the journey of others because every story is different. It's like comparing apples to oranges. There's no point. We've each just got to run the mile we're on.

CHAPTER 26

SPOON THEORY

"Do you wanna go grab lunch today?" I texted my friend, Leanna, who was home from OT school for the winter break. "I'd love to, but I don't think I have the energy today. I only had about thirty spoons today, and I promised my mom I'd go run some errands for her," she responded. "How about tomorrow?"

The spoon theory is a metaphor for disability that likens the fluctuations in energy levels that a person with disability faces on a daily basis to a set quantity of spoons.[45] For example, I could say that this morning I woke up with lots of energy (eighty spoons) and was able to make it to the gym first thing. This cost me thirty spoons. I did some cardio and strength training, and then ran some errands (twenty spoons) and made it out to dinner with a group of friends to celebrate a birthday (thirty spoons). Energy was high and I got a lot accomplished. I woke up with eighty spoons and

---

45 "What Is Spoon Theory?". 2020. *Healthline*. https://www.healthline.com/health/spoon-theory-chronic-illness-explained-like-never-before.

used them all. Yesterday, despite getting a full eight hours of sleep, I woke up sluggish and lethargic, and I had to make some difficult choices about how I expended my energy. Yesterday, I only woke up with thirty spoons. I didn't have enough energy in me to make it to a friend's barbecue or go on a two-mile walk (on top of my other activities for the day and my full-time job), so with the limited amount of energy I did have, I decided to read and do some arm exercises.

I find the spoon theory to be an interesting and accurate representation of the reality that is changing energy levels for a person with disability, and it takes on more meaning for me now than it ever did learning about it in school a few years ago. The difference being that now, it directly applies to me.

Sometimes I have good days, and sometimes I can barely get myself out of bed. But it's comforting to remember that each new day we wake up is a new chance, and maybe we'll wake up with more spoons tomorrow.

On days when I find myself with fewer spoons than usual, I find it helpful to prioritize my activities. Each morning, I identify and write down my Most Important Task. This is the one thing I absolutely must do for the day. If by the end of the day I've done nothing else, at least I will have accomplished my Most Important Task. Prioritizing, especially on days when I'm bogged down with fatigue, helps me feel that I'm still working toward my goals, even if I'm not crossing every item off of the to-do list.

Some days will be better than others, but as long as we are constantly striving toward our goals with one hundred spoons or five spoons, that is what counts. Let's make the most of the time and the spoons we have and use it to keep working for positive progress.

CHAPTER 27

SOMEONE TURN DOWN THE VOLUME

———

Terry Sullivan is another incredible stroke survivor friend of mine who lives in Geneva, Switzerland. For him, one of the biggest struggles poststroke has been dealing with over-stimulation and managing his seizures. "For example, if I go to the store and there are lots of aisles, I can't look because it's like my brain is processing too much information," he told me.[46]

One thing I think goes underappreciated by "normies" (a term fondly used by my fellow survivor friend Joe to describe those able-bodied people who have not suffered a stroke, brain injury, or other intense trauma) is just how difficult it can be to process information and deal with overstimulation. Things are different now; it is not uncommon to walk into a store and be overwhelmed with sensory overload. I don't get overwhelmed as much now by loud or busy venues, but that is partly because I started implementing a little trick.

———

46   Terry Sullivan, conversation with author, 23 July 2019.

When I find myself in a crowded or noisy situation and seeking an out, I always pause and take a second to collect myself. I walk to the bathroom or just close my eyes where I am and breathe. And sometimes if I need it, I give myself a little pep talk. *You can do this. There's nothing you can't handle! You've literally survived one of the most traumatic situations and you're still here ... just take a second to breathe and get back out there. You've got this.* Yeah, something like that.

When adapting to the new normal, it's so easy to fall into a cycle of negativity. Oftentimes, I find myself longing for the life I used to have and wishing I could do everything like I used to. So, I practice gratitude.

When I find myself going into this dark place, I take a second to reframe my perspective. Instead of focusing on the negative and the things I can no longer do, I call to mind things I'm grateful for. I have so many things to be grateful for. Waking up in the morning, having legs to balance and walk, a family who loves me and cares for me, the list goes on. Strokes, while definitely traumatic, can bring wonderful things and people into our lives that would not have been there otherwise.

In the case of Terry, his stroke convinced him to turn his life around and focus on his health. He dropped over a hundred pounds and found a newfound passion for fitness. I think that's pretty amazing and an excellent example of finding a new purpose when especially difficult challenges arise. Many people would not have the wherewithal to re-prioritize in a positive manner after multiple strokes and seizures. And yes, it's really easy to negatively spiral, so this is why it is so important to channel your energy, focus, and efforts on the things you *can* do and *can* control. Terry found a new purpose and interest in his health, which only helps him. Health is so important.

High blood pressure, cholesterol, diabetes, and smoking are all massive risk factors that could cause stroke. Knowing the risks and how to prevent them is the first step. I am so proud of Terry and his journey to refocus on his health and well-being. The doctors weren't sure what caused two of his arteries to spontaneously rupture and cause a stroke, but he has taken his health into his own hands and is searching for answers. I admire him tremendously for proactively taking an interest in his health and using his stroke as a vehicle to propel him forward and turn his life around.

"You can't just wait for doctors to tell you what you need to hear," NBA All-Star, Alonzo Mourning, shared with me. "You gotta get out there and educate yourself and try a little bit of everything if you have the ability," he continued.[47] His comment really resonated with me: *I am so blessed to have the opportunity to work hard at my recovery, and I realize that so many people don't get this chance. I have the ability, so why not make the most of it?*

The more we know, the more we can prevent accidents from happening. By being aware of the stroke risk factors, we will be more knowledgeable of how to take action. Terrible

---

47   Alonzo Mourning, conversation with author, 1 August 2019.

persisting headaches, severe pain, dizziness, and vision problems, all of these things could be signaling a stroke. And if it's not, well, at least you're taking control over your health.

So, if you ever experience anything like this, do yourself a favor and just go to the doctor. It's not normal to have a debilitating migraine that lasts over twenty days, and it could be a symptom of a larger problem, like an AVM in my case. The truth is that most strokes can be prevented, and taking the time to get a serious and lasting headache checked out could mean the difference between life and death. No joke. It sounds a bit intense and unnecessary, but it's not. I cannot emphasize enough how important it is to prioritize your health.

You're not guaranteed tomorrow, and today is the greatest gift and blessing you have. And if we want to increase our chances of waking up and experiencing tomorrow, we have to do everything we can today to make sure we get that opportunity.

That's the best advice I could give to anyone—don't take any chances on your health; it's too important. I myself have tried to take a page out of Terry's book and focus on my wellness goals. His secret? "I stopped eating carbs at night," he shared.[48] With focus and perseverance, we too can reach those seemingly impossible goals. If we first break it down step by step.

---

48   Terry Sullivan, conversation with author, 23 July 2019.

CHAPTER 28

THE HANGOVER PART IV

——

One of the biggest things I've come to learn about my new poststroke life is that the way I deal with fatigue is different now. Sure, I used to get tired like everyone else after a long day of studying or working. But I didn't *really* know what it meant to be fatigued until I experienced poststroke neuro fatigue. My survivor friend, Tawnie, explained it best: "It's like waking up with a splitting hangover every day."[49] You know the feeling of waking up with a hangover, and your brain feels all clouded and foggy? Well that's what it's like to be living under the influence of neuro fatigue. It's like a perpetual hangover or depleted battery life on your phone. I constantly need to switch on low power mode to preserve my energy.

Learning to manage this constant state of fogginess was a major adjustment. My mom likes to joke with me and ask, "Is anyone home?" No friend, lights are out, no one's home.

Over time, I've gotten better at dealing with this perpetual hangover. The key for me to overcome my groggy state (for

———
49   Tawnie Golic Cox, conversation with author, 29 September, 2019.

the most part, at least) has been constantly pushing my limits. But like Greg Nance says, it's not just about knowing your limits but respecting those limits, too.

In April of 2019, I began working my first full-time job. It was the ideal first postgrad job—a fifteen-minute commute and amazing opportunity to stay cognitively engaged with work I found to be interesting. Earlier that year, the opportunity presented itself to work full time, and as I hadn't really had a formal job yet since my stroke, I wasn't sure if I'd be able to handle it. But in classic Maddi fashion, I decided to just take the leap and jump in to the opportunity head-first. After all, I figured I wouldn't know what I was capable of unless I tried. And I'm so glad I did.

For those first few months while I was adjusting to working full time, I fatigued easier than I would have liked. Luckily, though, I was only working an eight-hour day and could go home to rest afterward. At this point I was also no longer in therapy, so any rehab exercises I did were on my own time. And as you can probably imagine, those first couple of months of adjusting to my new job did not see too much in terms of physical recovery advancements. But that was fine because I was learning how to balance work, exercises, my social life, and writing this book.

I have learned to respect my limits and understand that sometimes I'll need to pass up on something fun if my body tells me it needs a rest from the constant *go, go, go*. It's exhausting to be constantly switched *on*, and sometimes I just need a break from the whirlwind roller coaster that is my new life. So, I don't beat myself up for taking breaks to rest and recharge. I know my body will thank me.

PART 6:

A TREE GROWS IN BIRMINGHAM

CHAPTER 29

USE IT OR LOSE IT!

—————

The huge bucket of ice water sits across from me, filled to the brim. It's my first of three weeks at the Taub Clinic at the University of Alabama at Birmingham, and I have no idea what I've gotten myself into. My occupational therapist for the next few weeks returns with what appears to be a hand splint and a big smile. "Today we're going to start by trying a new strategy for weight bearing with that left arm," she tells me. "We're going to do an ice bath."

Okay, so that explains the mysterious bucket of ice and water in here. But what was an ice bath and how on earth was it going to help me?

* * *

Since my stroke, I'd been very fortunate in the sense that my body seemed to react well to whatever therapeutic intervention we tried: osteopathic manipulation to correct the rotated vertebrae in my neck (which is still a work in progress), or even Botox injections for the tone in my neck, arm, and leg that prevented normal muscle movements and caused my hand to flex and contract instead of open. I could send the message a million times from my brain to my hand, telling it to open, but my hand had a mind of its own. *Open,* I'd think, and instead it immediately does the opposite, tightening into a fist.

Muscle tone and the inability to effectively control the actions I wanted performed were my biggest challenges. This is why Botox was so important for me to get every couple of months. The Botox injection temporarily paralyzed the troublesome muscles, like my ankle, bicep, and finger flexors, so I could focus on strengthening them. Unfortunately, it's only a temporary fix.

I started getting injections six months after I had a stroke and found it extremely helpful, giving me extra time to focus on my rehab exercises without the intervention of unwanted muscle contractions. But after two months, I found that the Botox would wear off and my arm would get tight again. I wanted to correct this situation but wasn't sure how.

Which brings me back to the ice bath. That first week in Alabama, my occupational therapist told me that weight-bearing was the most important exercise I could do to rehabilitate my arm. I had a slight shoulder subluxation, which meant that the head of my humerus did not sit correctly in its position in the shoulder. Therefore, my shoulder joint was slightly dislocated. All of that being said, I was anxious to try any method that might help mitigate the negative effects of muscle tone, fix my shoulder position, and strengthen my arm.

My occupational therapist told me she wanted me to submerge my hand in the ice water up to my wrist five times in five second intervals. I did, and the intense cold of the water burned. We then dried off my hand and stretched my fingers, placing my hand into a weight-bearing splint. My hand went in easily, without its usual problems causing it to tighten.

With my hand easily secured in the splint, I did weight-bearing exercises to practice putting weight through my left hand. It was severely out of practice. After lots of weight-bearing exercises, I took my hand out of the splint and was surprised to see how loose my fingers were. My occupational therapist said the ice bath temporarily paralyzes the finger flexors, removing the tone from the equation so I would have a window of about thirty minutes or so to focus on finger activation while everything was nice and loose. An ice bath paired with weight-bearing is my secret to success. I can't go a day without it. If I don't get anything else done, weight-bearing is the one thing I absolutely must do. It has made all the difference in mitigating my tone.

Apart from weight-bearing, my three-week stint in Alabama also opened my eyes to the importance of using my affected side and incorporating it into daily activities. I had gotten by basically by just using my right hand for everything. I figured that because my left arm and hand were paralyzed, I might as well learn how to do everything with my other hand. But when I got to Alabama, this was not the case.

I was told I could *only* use my affected side to complete tasks while I was there. *Use it or lose it,* my therapist told me. It only takes a few days for the brain to rewire positively or negatively, and what had happened for me was that my brain decided that I didn't need to acknowledge my left side since it wasn't participating in any activities. But to positively rewire my brain, I needed to make an effort to incorporate my left hand into every activity I did, even if it couldn't actually help. Eventually, if I kept at it, there was the potential that my brain would rewire to acknowledge my left side, and the tasks would get easier. So, I began attempting to use my left side in tasks like opening and closing doors, zipping jackets, and tying my shoes.

Every morning while at the Taub Clinic at UAB, I would walk with my mom from our hotel to the Spain Rehabilitation Center. It was a fifteen-minute walk, and I enjoyed getting some walking in early in the day before switching to focus completely on my arm. One day, just outside the clinic, my mom noticed a very tiny tree sprouting up between the cracks in the pavement. "If that little tree can grow in the middle of a parking lot and flourish, you can draw strength from that tree and work hard to make progress in your recovery," my mom said.

So, every day while walking to the Taub Clinic, my mom and I looked out for our little tree. Every time I saw it, I thought, *If that tiny tree can grow in this parking lot, I can continue to recover. I am strong, like that little tree, and I can overcome this.*

The little tree reminded me of one of my favorite books as a child, *A Tree Grows in Brooklyn.* Except this time, it was in Birmingham. Recovery can be long, hard, and lonely, but us survivors are all in this together. I am here to support anyone who is struggling. The more we can band together and help one another by sharing our stories, the better, and the more lives we can positively impact.

CHAPTER 30

KEEP MOVING, THERE'S NOTHING TO SEE HERE

———

A wheelchair can be a special type of prison, but it can also be the vehicle that propels you to take your next step. Quite literally, this is what happened to me. The first time I sat up in a wheelchair, I was still in the hospital after my surgery. I spent fifteen days in a bed in the ICU, and my main accomplishment from this time was learning how to sit up. When you're completely paralyzed on one side, this is no small feat. It takes an incredible amount of energy for your body and brain to mobilize. A task as simple as sitting up requires many things to happen. You must have strong core strength to hold your body up as well as solid trunk support so your body doesn't sway. In other words, a lot of coordination needs to happen to sit up.

Initially, I lacked the strength to bring my body into a seated position. In the hospital, my physical therapist sat me in a wheelchair and forced me to sit upright in it for fifteen minutes at a time. It was the longest fifteen minutes of my life. I could barely do it, and afterward I was so tired that I had to get back in bed and rest. It was exhausting building up my stamina from scratch.

When you wake up one day to realize that you can't use one side of your body at all, it really makes you realize how much you once took for granted. I hated my wheelchair and wanted to do anything I could to get rid of it. But I couldn't learn to walk and ditch the wheelchair for good until I was able to first sit up.

So, I pushed myself a little bit each day; five more minutes, ten more minutes in the wheelchair, until sitting up was no problem. From here, the problem became building up stamina to start walking.

I desperately wanted to be able to walk and burn my wheelchair so I never had to use it again, but the intense physical exertion that walking cost me made me appreciate my wheelchair. I just got so tired from taking a few steps that I appreciated the opportunity to sit and rest.

When I started walking with a cane and venturing out into public to practice walking, I became hyperaware of how people stared at me. Here comes a girl with a cane struggling to walk, better steer clear! And oh, how people stared. Not only was it extremely rude, but it made me feel self-conscious, too. I wanted to say, *Look away, everyone. There's nothing to see here. I'm just trying to walk.* All I wanted was to look normal and not feel the prolonged stares from passersby. I get it. People aren't necessarily accustomed to seeing a young person with a cane, but I wanted to just tell everyone to f*** off. *Didn't your mother ever teach you that it's rude to stare?*

Clearly some people never got the memo. Or worse, thought they were being discreet, when in fact they were just more blatantly staring. Either way, it's still rude to stare, and I hated it.

So, I set a goal to work on the things that made me stand out, like not turning my head when I walk, or unconsciously bending my arm up. I wanted to normalize my walking so hopefully the stares would dissipate.

One day when I was walking with my mom, she noticed that I walked while blankly staring forward and not turning my head at all. "If you want to be natural," she said, "you have to practice turning your head a little when you walk. People tend to look around as they're walking."

She had a point. I had gotten so caught up in the physical act of walking that I was neglecting to head turn, which was equally as important. "A blank forward stare definitely signals to people that something is up," my mom said. I needed to be aware of everything around me, not just what was directly in front of me.

While I didn't like what my mom had to say because I hated turning my head, I knew she was right. Maybe it was because of the tightness in my neck, but I didn't like to move it around, especially to the left side. It felt like a chore to turn my head, so I just didn't do it. Maybe this is what was holding me back from having the "normal" life I so desired.

I wouldn't call myself an extremely vain person, but I do to some extent care about how I am perceived poststroke. My stroke survivor friend, Terry, articulated a similar sentiment. For him, his stroke made him reevaluate how much he cared about what others thought of him, and made him focus on what was actually important.

"I take pleasure in much smaller things in life," he told me. "Like flowers, I take pictures of flowers."[50] What Terry and I have both come to realize is how important the simple pleasures of life are. Spending time with loved ones, reading a book, drawing a picture, whatever it is that gives you joy, just do it. Life is simply too short not to. If there's anything you take away from this chapter, I hope it's that you find ways to have a greater appreciation for the little things. Oh, and don't stare. It's rude.

---

50   Terry Sullivan, conversation with author, 23 July 2019.

CHAPTER 31

TURNING LEMONS TO LEMONADE

The road to recovery can be long and lonesome, which is why it is so important and helpful to have a strong support system. I realize I am very lucky to have family and friends who have supported me from day one. Two years into my recovery journey, I realized that I was ready to pay it forward and share my story to encourage and inspire others. I had reached a stage in my recovery journey where I was ready to engage with fellow survivors and actually talk about my experience. Whereas before I just wanted distance from my brain injury, now I was ready to participate in the brain injury community and give back to others like me. I wanted to show that recovery is possible, even if it doesn't happen exactly how you would like. With this new goal to help others in mind, I set out to connect with other survivors. There had to be a community out there somewhere of young stroke survivors, and I was going to find it.

A lot of misconceptions exist about stroke patients. I take it as a compliment when people I meet are surprised to hear that I had a stroke and at such a young age. After having gone through this traumatic experience, I want to focus my efforts on dispelling the misconceptions and educating people about the reality of life after stroke. I've met some amazing people doing awesome work to spread awareness of stroke and brain injury. I am connecting with people around the world who share with me their stories of brain injury and how they recover.

Many people, including me prior to my brain hemorrhage, mistakenly think that strokes only happen to old people. *Wrong.* I am living proof that that is not true. Over the past two and a half years I have met so many young people like me who had a stroke or brain injury. It is much more common than you would think. The reality of the situation is that life is short, fragile, and we don't know what tomorrow has in store. We don't even know *if* there will be a tomorrow. Let's live each day to the fullest, and not take a single moment of the day for granted. 2,522,880,000 seconds, remember?

* * *

Bridget Chiovari is a fellow AVM stroke survivor in Arizona, and she is one of the first people I connected with through Instagram. We immediately hit it off, and I was thrilled to discover that we shared a similar perspective on life post brain injury.

"It's so important to be vocal about [brain injury] and just put it out there that, yeah, this could happen," Bridget told me.[51] And I couldn't agree more. On my final day of constraint

---

51   Bridget Chiovari, phone conversation with author, 28 July 2019.

therapy down in Alabama, I created a new Instagram account to share all my recovery progress photos and videos. In tandem with my new Instagram, I launched a blog to share my stories of recovery and future goals.[52]

Through the blog and Instagram, I'm talking constantly with people around the world who share the common experience of recovery from trauma. We are a family. The brain injury community is incredible, and I wonder now why I didn't put myself out there and get involved sooner. I never would have met so many amazing people if my life had gone as I had originally planned. I would probably be living up in Boston as I had anticipated but still grappling with the big questions of purpose. My brain injury has given me a renewed sense of purpose. I never would have thought it could be possible, but it is, and therefore I am so grateful for my injury.

A whole world of opportunity exists out there at our disposal if we just take the time to look. We have the power to turn the obstacles we face into amazing opportunities. It's all up to us.

Now that I'm out there and actively participating in the stroke community, I can't imagine my life any other way. I am grateful to be a part of such a close-knit community with people who share the same mission to change the face of stroke and raise awareness, one survivor at a time.

---

52   "Maddistrokeofluck". 2020. *Maddistrokeofluck*. https://maddistroke-ofluck.com/.

CHAPTER 32

TODAY IS A BEAUTIFUL DAY TO BE ALIVE

———

As I just mentioned, immediately after my stroke, I had zero desire to connect with other survivors. I just wanted to distance myself from my experience with brain injury as much as I could. I was nervous that this brain injury would come to define me, and I wanted to show everyone that I was more than my injury. I didn't want to be *that girl*. I am so much more than one small setback.

It wasn't until two years later that I finally realized what I was missing in my recovery: connection with others who had gone through the same thing I had. So, I set out to add value to a community of survivors who could support each other and share effective strategies for daily living. The question I was dying to answer was, as survivors of stroke and brain injury, how can we use our life experience to help and inspire others, show what's possible with recovery, and educate "the normies" about our experience and hopefully get them to understand what happened to us could happen to anyone?

Seeing as I was initially anxious to distance myself from my stroke, for a while I was hesitant to join any form of stroke support group and meet other survivors. The way that I saw it, this one experience does not define me, and I will not let it. I am still very much the same person, just with less mobility and more fatigue.

But when I finally decided that I was ready to share my experience and learn from others, I wasn't sure where to start. So, true to form like the Gen Z'er I am, I took to Instagram. I followed stroke-related hashtags and found the people who were being vocal in the brain injury community.

It really is a community. I have met and spoken with so many other survivors who share the same struggles as me. That's how I met Bridget, who agreed that, "building up a positive community is huge."[53]

For me and Bridget, a fellow AVM stroke survivor, our strokes have given us a new perspective on life that we would not have had otherwise. "I literally live every single day like I am going to die tomorrow because I have a stupid thing in my brain. So, it's like, I never know what's going to happen," she says.[54]

I appreciated my life before the stroke, but the difference now is that I am hyperaware of the fragility of life, having come so close to having it taken away from me. I firmly believe there is a reason I lived and a reason I'm still on this earth today.

53   Bridget Chiovari, phone conversation with author, 28 July 2019.
54   (Bridget Chiovari, phone conversation with author, 28 July 2019.

And just maybe it's so I can use my experience to help better the lives of others.

Hearing Bridget's new poststroke view on life deeply resonated with me: "Holy s**t, I just had a second chance at life. A lot of people don't get this. And I need to be grateful for it."[55]

But that can be easier said than done. I know this to be true. And yet, I wake up every single morning and the first thing I do is remind myself: *Today is a beautiful day to be alive. Every day we wake up is a blessing, and each moment of every day presents us with a unique set of circumstances and choices. It is up to me to make the most of it and decide how I will live because I might not get another day. So, why not be present and make the absolute most of the current moment because that is all we have.*

---

55   (Bridget Chiovari, phone conversation with author, 28 July 2019.

CHAPTER 33

BRAIN BUDDIES

Instagram has been an amazing tool for me in my recovery. Through social media, I have been able to connect with so many other stroke survivors to both learn from them and help in turn by sharing my own story. I am now a part of an amazing group of stroke survivors who call ourselves the Brain Buddies. We hop on Skype calls once a week to talk about what is going on in our lives. Everyone is at different stages of recovery, but we all share a common experience and desire to use our journey to help others. I am so grateful for my Brain Buddies; they continuously open my eyes to struggles I never considered and creative new strategies for managing the challenges we face.

We Brain Buddies love to chat because, in a way, our conversations are better and more helpful than any form of therapy. Things like socializing or processing what has happened to us can be difficult, so it's great to have an outlet to share our struggles with those who understand what it's like. It can be an isolating experience to go through alone, so it is important to have people you can count on who will be there to help and support you on the good days and the bad.

Thank you Adrian, Bridget, Courtney, Darren, Jamie, Kristin, Leah, Joe, Michelle, Mimi, and Zolly for being there to support me on this journey. I only hope that one day I'm able to help all of you as much as you have helped me.

Now you may be surprised to hear this, but I *hate* going to therapy. I hate the fact that I can't do things like I used to and that I need to put in the effort to get better. *You mean I actually have to try? I'm not just going to recover on my own? God forbid I have to actually make an effort.* But, *of course,* I wasn't going to get better unless I put in the hours, weeks, months, and years of hard work.

Although I hated going to therapy, I found ways to make it more enjoyable. Connecting with my fellow patients, other therapists, caregivers, and staff members made my weekly therapy a little more enjoyable. I was subconsciously building my network of fellow members of the brain injury community.

When I first started my stroke Instagram account, I made an effort to follow all the relevant hashtags and reach out to at least one new stroke survivor every day. After a couple hundred DMs and FaceTime conversations, I found I no longer needed to commit to this goal. My community was growing organically. I was receiving lots of messages from stroke survivors around the world, people I had never met before. And they all had different aspects of recovery that they wanted to discuss. I'm no doctor or therapist, but I can share what has helped me because maybe it would help someone else, too. I'm growing a community of stroke survivors on Instagram, and it gives me a sense of purpose. I just want other survivors and thrivers to know that no matter how bad it gets, you always have something to be thankful for and appreciate. We have so much to live for, and if you ever find yourself going to a dark place and unable to find the positives in your life, just give me a call. Remember, you are not alone. No matter what you are battling, I promise you, you have something to live for.

CHAPTER 34

NO BETTER TIME
THAN THE PRESENT

———

Joe Borges is a fellow stroke survivor, co-host of the *Neu-roNerds* podcast, and one of the first survivors I connected with through the Gram. He understands how important it is to use the stroke experience to help others and have the most positive impact. "Anytime I feel like I can't do this, I think of the community. This is bigger than just for me. I have a platform that other people just don't have. I have an opportunity and a voice," Joe told me.[56]

As survivors, we have a voice and what I believe to be a moral obligation to use our experience to help others. I am learning that so many amazing people are out there doing just that and touching the lives of so many people. And I want to do my part.

———

56   Joe Borges, phone conversation with author, 20 July, 2019.

It's amazing how much simply hearing the journeys of others can inspire you to make positive changes to your own. Every fellow brain injury survivor I have connected with has inspired me in some way to keep working toward recovery.

James Clear is an author and entrepreneur who has written extensively on habit building. When I first read his book, *Atomic Habits,* I was struck by his message. If we want to see positive change in our lives, we need to develop effective systems to help us achieve our goals.

"Every action you take is a vote for the type of person you wish to become," James Clear writes. "No single instance will transform your beliefs, but as the votes build up, so does the evidence of your new identity."[57]

When I think about it that way, my life suddenly takes on an increased sense of urgency. If every single action we take contributes to the type of person we ultimately become, shouldn't we constantly strive toward becoming the best person we can be? Shouldn't we take those little actions daily that will bring us one step closer to that person, until we wake up one morning to discover that we *are* that person?

If you feel passionately about something, take action today. Even if it's just five minutes. The important thing is that you

---

57 "Atomic Habits: An Easy & Proven Way to Build Good Habits & Break Bad Ones". 2020. *James Clear.* https://jamesclear.com/atomic-habits.

do *something* and start building the habit of putting in the work. The last thing we want is to wake up fifty years from now and regret never having worked on what was supposedly important to us. If I can do it, you can do it. We all can do it. The hardest part is just taking that first step.

CHAPTER 35

SURVIVOR SUNDAY

———

My stroke survivor friend, Joe, introduced me to a fellow brain injury survivor who changed my life in the best way possible. When I first FaceTimed Tawnie Golic-Cox, a brain aneurysm survivor who lives in California, she told me I was the first survivor she had talked to on the phone. I was honored. We found it to be such a beneficial experience to share our journeys with each other that we decided to continue the conversation weekly. Tawnie convinced me to try going Instagram live, and we made a plan to hold weekly live streams we called "Survivor Sunday," to discuss our recovery and share strategies.

I'm not going to lie. The first time I went Instagram live with her felt really awkward and I wasn't sure what I was doing. Essentially, we FaceTimed each other for an hour and followers could tune in and watch our conversation. They could also comment while we were talking. I was so thrown off at first by the fact that people were writing comments while we were talking, and it was a real exercise in visual scanning for me to multitask and read the comments while carrying on a conversation with Tawnie. It was really hard, but the more we held live streams, the more people tuned in and shared their stories with us, and the better I got at multitasking.

Instagram live automatically shuts down after an hour, and I found that as I became more comfortable with going live, the time would fly by and we would hit the hour mark and get shut down before finishing our conversation. But I see that as a good thing. It means we were having a productive chat and engaging with our audience. And our audience is growing.

Going Instagram live has been a great way for me to work on my executive functioning skills. After the stroke, my working memory was horrendous, so I needed to build it back up from scratch. Lots of memory exercises and journaling definitely helped with that, but I've found that the best form of cognitive therapy has been real-life activities and tasks with cognitive benefits that don't feel like therapy at all.

Working a job, writing this book, going Instagram live—all of these activities and more have practical application to my life and my recovery. The more practice I got with multitasking for Survivor Sundays—reading Instagram live comments and carrying on a conversation—the better I got.

This is something that is much harder for me now than it ever was pre-stroke. I used to be able to seamlessly jump between topics in a conversation, plan activities last minute, and work on multiple projects simultaneously. No more. These days, I need to put all my focus into one activity at a time. But that being said, I've been pleased with the improvements I am making in multitasking during the Survivor Sunday live streams.

Ultimately, the goal of Survivor Sundays has been to help others. We're all surviving something—life. So even if you're not a stroke survivor, the lessons and takeaways from Survivor Sundays can still be directly applied to your life. Tawnie and I aim to spread the message of positivity, which has helped us personally so much in our recovery journeys.

And we're not the only ones. "That was my goal, to take the negative going on in my life and turn it into a positive, inspiring people," Alonzo Mourning told me.[58] This is my goal, too; if I could help even just one person by sharing my story, I know my life would be complete. I could die happy. Tawnie and I both thought there had to be a way that good could come out of our experiences and the knowledge we had accumulated during our recovery could help someone else. And that was the motivation for us starting Survivor Sunday.

While social media and Instagram have so many negatives to them, at the same time they are also tremendous tools and platforms for positivity if we choose to use them in the right way. In this sense, I think social media has been an amazing benefit to me in my recovery journey. Connecting with other survivors like Tawnie through Instagram and Facebook has really been life changing, and it reinforced in me the idea that we are a community and family brought together by a shared experience. We may all have different and unique stories about our injuries and recovery, but we all share a common goal to get better. Sometimes, just talking to someone and having someone listen to you share your struggles, even if they don't have an answer to them, can

---

58　(Alonzo Mourning, conversation with author, 1 August 2019).

mean so much. Knowing someone out there cares and is on your team makes all the difference.

"Please keep doing what you're doing. Keep writing. Keep putting those words of inspiration on paper," Alonzo Mourning said to me right before we hung up. Maybe he was right; maybe I would be doing God a disservice to not share my journey. So, I approached my book project with a renewed passion and desire to help as many other survivors as I could.

CHAPTER 36

ONWARD!

People often ask me: *How did you have the strength to work toward your goals for recovery and maintain a positive attitude? I don't think I could do it.* The simple fact of the matter is that anyone would be able to. You really don't know what you are capable of until you deal with an incredible challenge or life obstacle.

And you *will* deal with it. You have no other choice. We all possess an insane amount of strength within us, and oftentimes we don't even realize we have this until a situation that tests our abilities presents itself. I said I didn't want to get too religious in this book, but in all honesty, my faith has played a huge part in my recovery.

My renewed faith after my stroke has brought me into contact with old friends I haven't seen in years as well as new ones, and we share a common perspective on life. I'm not happy that I had a stroke, but I am happy and grateful for all the people who have come into my life because of it. I am so lucky to have friends literally all over the world that I can always talk to and share my struggles and victories with while hearing about their journeys too.

So many crazy things have happened poststroke that never would have happened otherwise. For example, I have become good friends with a young woman my age who lives in Skopje, Macedonia, and when we FaceTime she teaches me Macedonian phrases. те сакам, Marija.

Or my friend Lena who lives in Denmark. Lena taught me the importance of not overextending yourself. "Now I am focused," she told me.[59] "I don't do extra jobs or things I don't want to do."[60] Like Lena, I have been making a concerted effort to not take on too many activities so I can focus on what is actually important to me. I am learning how to say no to others when I have too much on my plate and take the time to focus on myself—my mental health, my spiritual and physical well-being, my job, this book, and connecting with other survivors.

The stroke and brain injury community really is a family, and I'm so thankful to be a part of it and have a huge network of friends all across the globe to chat with who share a common experience. Stroke sucks. There's no denying it, but it sucks less when you have an incredible support system to share those struggles with. You're not alone, and many people are out there struggling along the same journey. If you or someone you know is looking for a reason to continue on the road to recovery, please reach out to me on Instagram

---

59   (Lena Elsborg, conversation with author, 18 January 2020).

60   (Lena Elsborg, conversation with author, 18 January 2020).

(@maddistrokeofluck) or by email (maddiniebanck@gmail.com) because I'd love to connect and chat. The whole world is filled with positive-minded survivors who can relate and help turn anyone's mood around.

Over the past couple of years, I have turned to my Brain Buddies and other members of the stroke community for support along the journey. And now I firmly believe it is my mission to do the same for other people.

As I write this, I am reminded of my conversation with NBA All-Star, Alonzo Mourning. When we spoke, he fervently told me that we were all put on this earth for a reason, with the duty to serve and to live our lives on God's path. And Alonzo Mourning, the elite athlete and philanthropic advocate for kidney disease, is living out this mission and finding his purpose. "That was my goal, to take the negative going on in my life and turn it into a positive and inspire people. We're all here to serve."[61]

Amen.

---

61   Alonzo Mourning, conversation with author, 1 August 2019.

CHAPTER 37

EPILOGUE

———

As I sit at my desk writing this final chapter on a cold November morning, six months shy of my three-year stroke anniversary and five months away from publication, I am overwhelmed with gratitude and appreciation for everyone who has been a part of the journey in some way. Today, I can do so many things that I thought were impossible two years ago.

When I reflect on the journey of the past three years, the advances I have made in that time are monumental. Suddenly all those daily frustrations are meaningless because look where that hard work has gotten me. There was a time when I was lying paralyzed in a hospital bed in the ICU, unsure if I would ever walk or move my arm again. Fast forward two years and I'm juggling a full-time job with my cardio and strengthening exercises and writing my second book. The last time I published a book I wasn't working, so I had more time to devote to it. You could say writing the book and focusing on therapy *was* my job.

When I put it that way, it really makes me realize how blessed I am to have had the opportunity to get to this point. Getting to a point where I'm back to doing activities I enjoy and feeling like a contributing member of society is amazing. I love my job, my family and friends, my therapists, and every single person who has supported me along the way. If you got anything out of this book, I hope I have been able to show you that anything is possible. I would use myself as an example to anyone struggling through an obstacle, health-related or not, and say that you are way stronger than you may think you are. You don't know what you're capable of until you try.

If you had asked me three years ago where I thought I would be today; it certainly would not have been here. I never would have imagined I'd be a published author, and of not one book, but two books! And I certainly never would have anticipated the fact that even after my stroke, I would be able to write a significant portion of my second book using two hands instead of one.

———————

If everything had gone as planned, I'd be living and working up in Boston and never would have found the amazing job I have now. See, everything happens for a reason, and so many incredible things have happened to me as a result of my stroke. I have met some incredible people—therapists, doctors, patients, coworkers—who care about me and are invested in my recovery. I have found an incredible community of brain injury survivors, and chatting with these friends is always the highlight of my week. I jumped headfirst into a full-time job and have loved every minute of it. While sometimes crazy busy, I have no complaints and I am grateful for the learning opportunity. I have a job I enjoy, with people I like; it's almost more than I could ask for. I feel so blessed.

I've come a long way from waking up completely paralyzed on my left side almost three years ago. At that point, I don't think anyone could have told you where I would be now, or how much I would manage to recover. If there's one thing I've learned through all of this, it is that no one knows the future—not even the doctors.

I had heard from multiple sources that the majority of recovery from stroke happens in the first six to eighteen months post-injury. I can tell you confidently that this is a flat out lie. Recovery is a lifelong process, and don't let anyone tell you what your limits are or what your limitations will be after X amount of time. *No one knows for sure.*

I would argue that I made the majority of my recovery after this eighteen-month mark while at the Taub Clinic for stroke rehab at UAB. The most crucial lesson I learned there was to cultivate the habit of use. And, understandably, the more you engage that affected side in daily activities, the more natural it becomes.

I would like to end this book with one final note. If your goals are not progressing as quickly as anticipated, that is absolutely okay. Our lives are not static, and our paths are bound to change. I'm not in Boston like I thought, but arguably I'm in an even better place. My goals and aspirations for my life's work have slightly changed, and I am learning to love the journey. Each moment of each day is a brand-new opportunity, so let's be sure to take advantage of that. Onward!

STRATEGIES

———

So, I told a little white lie. The previous chapter was not the end of the book. This is. To end this book, I wanted to share some of the exercises and strategies that have helped me in my recovery so you can try them yourself and see what works for you.

I'm not a therapist, but these exercises were given to me by the therapists I've had over the past few years, and they all have helped advance my recovery in some way. I hope they can help you like they have helped me.

FOR THE LOWER EXTREMITY:[62]
The following is a list of exercises that were given to me upon completion of The Taub Therapy Clinic training program for the lower extremity. My therapist at the Taub Clinic instilled in me the belief that regular exercise is critical to maintaining the gains I made while in the program. While it is very difficult to get through all of these exercises every single day, at the very least I make an effort to stretch and walk. Stretching

———

62   (Danna Kay King and Mary Bowman, Taub Clinic Home exercise
      program for author, 2019).

in particular is extremely important in improving mobility and flexibility. I stretch my ankle every single day.

Also please note that I am writing these exercises from the perspective of a person who is left-side affected, so if your affected side is the right and not the left, use the opposite side from what is written in this portion of the book.

Ankle/Foot Dorsiflexion stretch: Otherwise known as the runners stretch. Stand with your left foot behind the right in a staggered stance. Place a small object like a folded towel under the toes of your left foot so they are extended. While keeping the heel of your left foot completely on the floor and your right knee bent, stretch your left ankle five times for fifteen seconds.

WARMUP:

Left hip abduction while lying on the right side (side leg lift): Lie on your right side. Roll hips forward. Place left leg slightly behind the right leg. Lift your left leg up toward the ceiling while keeping the knee straight. Do two sets of ten.

Internal rotation: Lie on your back with both legs straight and slightly apart. Rotate both legs inward to touch the toes of right and left feet together. Then relax, letting your legs roll back. Do two to three sets of ten.

Lower trunk rotations (you might want to do this one on a slightly cushiony surface like a bed or a padded mat): Lie on your back with your hips and knees bent and your feet flat on the ground. Gently rotate your knees to your left side as far as you can. Then rotate your knees back to the right side as far as you can. Keep your upper body and shoulders flat on the bed during this exercise. Do three sets of five.

Bridges (best to do on a cushiony surface like a bed): Lie on your back with both knees bent and feet flat on the surface. Lift your hips up off the surface as high as possible. Make sure you do not twist and you keep the right side of your pelvis even with the left side of your pelvis. Do three sets of ten.

To advance this exercise: Lie on your back with the left side of your body at the edge of the bed. Lower your left leg over the edge of the bed with knee bent and place left foot on a stool or on the floor. Press down on the stool with your left foot to lift your left hip off of the bed. Do two sets of ten.

If you want another variation of this exercise, lift your left foot onto the bed. While lying on your back with the left side of your body at the edge of the bed, lower your left leg over the side of the bed with your knee bent. Lift your left leg up, bending at the hip and knee and lift your toes. Place your foot onto the bed. Then lower your left leg back to the start position. Make sure the left knee remains bent and does not collapse to the side during these movements. Concentrate on lifting your toes as you start movement in both directions (up to the bed and down off the bed). Do two sets of ten.

Walking inside: Walk for practice every day. If you are able to take a step, take as many as possible. When walking indoors, remember to shift your weight onto your left leg and grow tall over your left leg. Take a nice long, smooth step with the right leg. When stepping with your left foot, lift toes (including outside of toes) and try to place your heel down first. Focus on trying to prevent hip hiking of the left side of your hip/pelvis.

Walking outside: Find a safe place to walk at least 200 feet outside on grass or sidewalk. The varying surfaces are going to be challenging to your balance. Always remember to try and put your heel down first when you step with your left foot. Do not let your left ankle invert. Always try to shift your weight completely onto the left leg and foot, growing tall over your left leg before you take a step with the right foot. Progress the distance and frequency as you are able.

Stairs: Go up and down a flight of stairs with a sturdy hand-rail. When ascending the stairs, try to prevent twisting or hiking your hip when stepping up with the left foot. Try to bend your left hip and knee as much as possible. Be sure to shift your weight onto the left leg before taking a step with the right leg.

Left foot on stool: Stand with a four-inch stool in front of you. Lift your left foot and place it on top of the stool. Be sure to lift your toes and bend your knee. Try to prevent hip hiking. Then bring your left foot back down to the floor. Repeat this motion for thirty seconds or until you have completed ten touches. Do at least five sets. You can make this task harder by increasing the height of the stool, increasing the number of times you place your foot on the stool, and increasing the distance of the stool from your foot.

Place right foot on stool: This is the same exercise as the above except with your opposite (right) foot stepping up onto the stool. This is a good exercise to practice stabilizing your weight over your left leg while stepping up with your right. Perhaps the most important thing I learned from one and a half years of physical therapy was how to weight shift and accept my weight on my left side. I had been compensating, unwilling to distribute my weight equally while walking. And for the most part, I wasn't even really aware that I was refusing to accept weight on my left. My therapist, Todd, told me countless times to shift my weight to the left, but it just didn't click. But when I was in Alabama, we focused intensely on weight shifting, and my gait improved.

Step to stool to your left side: Place a stool or a block of wood that is about four inches high to the side of your left foot. Lift your left foot and place it on the stool, focusing on preventing twisting or hip hiking. Then step back to the floor with your left foot. Be sure to lift your left toes when placing your foot on the stool and when bringing it back down to the floor. Do this for about thirty seconds or until you have placed your left foot on the stool about ten times. Do at least five sets. You can make this task more difficult by increasing the height of the stool and/or the number of times you place your foot on the stool.

Stepping over objects: In life, we do not always walk on a perfectly flat surface. For this reason, it is important to practice managing varying terrain surfaces and stepping over objects you may encounter in your path. If your house is anything like mine, you have messy rooms and, therefore, ample opportunities to practice stepping over articles of clothing in your path. For this exercise, place four to five items on the floor. The objects should not be more than a couple of inches tall. I will typically use rolled-up towels to practice stepping over. Walk forward and step over the objects with your left foot first and then turn around and head back with the right foot leading. Be sure to lift your toes and bend your knee. This task can be made more difficult by increasing the size of the object over which you are stepping or by increasing the number of repetitions.

Sometimes when I am walking outside, I'll collect little twigs or rocks to throw in my path so I can practice stepping over them. Life can be a bumpy road with unexpected obstacles. Sometimes things get in our way. So that is why it is important to practice managing the varying surfaces we might encounter.

Side step to the left and right: Stand facing a counter. Step to the right for twenty feet and then step back to the left for twenty steps. Perform five times in each direction. Try to decrease the number of steps required to go twenty feet. Remember to stand tall and keep your toes pointed toward the counter and your body facing the counter. Do not turn sideways. Try not to drag your toes on your left foot. You can make this task more difficult by walking farther or by increasing the number of repetitions.

Left leg marching: Stand with a counter to your side and hold the counter for stability. Lift your left leg up toward your chest, bending your left knee as if you are marching. Lift your left leg as much as you are able to without hip hiking. Do five sets of five.

Pick up an object from the floor and place it on a high shelf slightly to your left: When you stoop to pick up an object from the floor, make sure you are putting equal weight on both of your legs. When you stand up, shift your weight onto your left leg and then reach. Do this five times.

Balance on left leg: With your hand on the counter for balance, lift your right leg so you are balancing completely on your left leg. Try to lift your hand off of the counter as you are able to. Do this at least five times and then switch legs.

Tandem balance: Standing next to the counter, place your feet in tandem stance with the left foot in front. Try to keep your balance and lift your hands off of the counter as you are able. Then swap positions of your feet so that your right foot is in front. Try to balance for longer periods of time.

Step to X's with right foot: I love this exercise because, for a left-side affected person like me, this activity forces me to shift my weight onto my left side. I had grown accustomed to favoring my right side when I walked and spent as little time as possible on my left side while walking. The more that we focus on engaging that affected side, the better our gait will get.

For this exercise, start with your feet approximately shoulder-width apart. Step forward to a mark about ten inches in front of you with the right foot. Then return to your starting position. Next, step out to the right side to a mark about ten inches to the side of your right foot. Then return to the start position. Finally, step backward to a mark about ten inches behind your right foot. Then return to the start position. Repeat this pattern for thirty seconds. Do five sets. Make sure you shift your weight onto the left leg before you move the right foot. Do not let your hips twist. You can make this task more challenging by increasing the distance of the X's from the original start position.

Step to X's with left foot: This activity is the same as the one above except with the targets on your left side as you step with your left foot and stabilize with the right.

Walk backward: I hate this exercise and I am terrible at it, but it is a good one to strengthen hamstrings and hip extensors. Walk backward ten feet. Make sure you lift your left toes and bend your left knee when stepping back with the left foot. Do this five times.

Step up onto a stool on the left side: Stand facing a counter for safety. Place a four-inch stool to the side of your left foot. Lift your left foot and place it on the stool. Then step up on the stool with your right foot. Step back down with your right foot and bring your left foot back to the floor. When you step up onto the stool with your left foot first, be sure to step far enough to leave room for your right foot to join. Be sure to shift your weight onto the left foot after placing it on the stool and before you lift your right foot to the stool. Grow tall over your left leg.

Ramp walking: Practice walking up and down a ramp, shifting your weight to the left and making sure to put your heel down first when stepping with your left foot. You can also practice walking sideways up and down a ramp. Walk up the ramp leading with your left foot and then back down leading with your right. Try to take big steps and don't drag your toes. Be sure to shift your weight onto your left side.

Walking while carrying pillows: I also hate this exercise, but it's a good one because it involves the upper extremity as well. Start in a seated position and hold a couple of pillows in both hands. If one of your hands doesn't work that well (like my left), I still get my left arm involved by squishing the pillows to my chest. I wrap my right hand around the pillows to grab them too so I'm holding them with two hands. As long as your affected arm is somehow staying engaged, that's good.

With the pillows in your hands, stand up with equal weight bearing on both legs. Walk forward fifteen steps and turn around and walk back to the chair. Sit back down on the chair and then repeat. Do this five to ten times. This is a great exercise to practice equal weight-bearing when moving from a seated position to standing. The key is to maintain equal weight distribution on both legs when standing and walking.

Step up and down a curb: This practical exercise also has real life applications. Oftentimes when we are out walking, we will need to step down from a curb or step up onto a sidewalk. (Make sure someone is standing by you when you first attempt this exercise in case you need help.) Step up onto a curb leading with your right foot. Step down from the curb leading with your left foot. Then alternate.

FOR THE UPPER EXTREMITY:[63]
The following is a list of exercises that were given to me as a home exercise program following my three weeks at the Taub Clinic at the University of Alabama at Birmingham in

---

63　(Danna Kay King and Mary Bowman, Taub Clinic Home exercise program for author, 2019).

July of 2019. The following exercises are meant to promote continuous recovery by encouraging neuroplasticity and positive brain change. The way my therapist, Mary, put it, each activity you perform with your affected side is adding to your recovery and brain change. It is similar to adding coins in a bank. Each time you use your affected arm and hand, the change adds up in the brain.

Mary also told me that brain change is use-dependent, meaning that whatever you use your affected arm and hand to do is what changes your brain in a positive way. The Taub Clinic research has shown that "you can continue to make progress as long as you continue to use your affected arm and hand for daily activities and continue to challenge yourself with your home program activities."[64] When retraining your brain after stroke, the absolute most important thing is to practice safe and functional use of your affected side in your everyday life. The following activities have helped me in my recovery and I still continue to do and improve upon them. I hope they can be of help to you as well. Good luck.

Warm up of scapula and shoulder muscles: To start your day off right, do some shoulder movements in the morning. To mobilize the shoulders and scapula, practice shrugging your shoulders while in a seated position and then rolling your shoulders back while drawing elbows inward. Do each exercise ten times.

Active reaching movements: A good way to warm up and start your day by engaging your affected side (going forward I will

---

64   (Mary Bowman, conversation with author, 12 June 2019).

say "left side" because that's what it is for me, but if you are right-side affected, use your right arm) is to practice actively reaching for targets. This is also a good time to state your morning affirmations: Today is a beautiful day to be alive. For example:

- Reach to touch your mouth with your middle finger.
- Reach down to touch your right foot and toes.
- Touch the top of your head with your palm down.
- Reach to touch your left foot and toes.
- Touch the top of your right shoulder.
- Touch your left ear with your palm back.
- Reach to touch the lumbar area of your back.

I believe a strong warm-up routine sets you up for success throughout the day. While I don't always get around to completing the shoulder and scapula warmups every day, without a doubt, weight-bearing is one activity I have to do.

Sometimes, I'm tired after a long day at work and don't feel that I have it in me to do arm or leg exercises. However, I absolutely need to do my weight-bearing. Weight-bearing is a great exercise to stimulate your proprioceptors and signal to the brain that it needs to use this arm and hand.

My therapist in Alabama taught me this helpful trick that I do every single day to help with tone management. Every morning, before I do anything else, I take an ice bath. The ice bath relaxes my hand for about thirty minutes so I can do weight-bearing and active reaching exercises without the influence of excessive flexor tone. The weight-bearing and the ice bath both relax my hand so it is able to cooperate more with the exercises.

To do an ice bath: I fill a large pitcher with ice and water and then I dunk my left hand into the pitcher up to my wrist five times for five seconds. This is such a quick and easy thing to do that has immediate implications on my muscle tone. After my ice bath, I dry off my hand with a towel and slide it into a weight-bearing splint. The weight-bearing splint is essentially a padded splint just for my hand. While my hand is relaxed, I put it into the weight-bearing splint and wrap it up. The weight-bearing splint essentially keeps my hand and fingers in a straight position so I am able to focus on pushing weight through it. Once my weight-bearing splint is on, I move into the exercises. Seated at the couch, I do the following:

- Press in and out with my hand on an ottoman in front of me. I do three sets of ten reps. After this, I move into a prolonged press and hold forward on the ottoman. Three sets of ten.
- With my hand next to me, I press my left hand into the cushion, shifting my weight to the left side as I do so. While keeping my elbow straight, I load my weight through my left arm and hand. Three sets of ten. The weight-bearing splint is helpful for this task because it keeps my fingers in good alignment. If necessary, place a folded washcloth under the heel of your hand to lessen how far your wrist needs to extend. This task can be advanced by shifting to the left side and simultaneously raising your right hip.
- With your left arm still positioned next to you on the couch, shift your weight over onto the left arm and raise

your right hand to reach across your body and to a target. Three sets of ten.

- Lying prone on the floor with your legs out straight and resting on your elbows, move side to side so that your scapulas and shoulders move with you. This is a good weight-shifting exercise. You can also transition to your knees with your hands extended straight in front of you and palms flat on the floor. From this position rock side to side, making sure to shift weight onto your left completely when rocking in that direction. From this position you can also practice modified push-ups while keeping your weight equally distributed between your left and right sides. Three sets of ten for each.

All of these weight-bearing exercises can be modified depending on what resources you have available to you. Sometimes I practice the hands and knees weight-bearing exercise while standing over a table or chair, or against a wall. It may sound weird, but honestly doing these weight-bearing exercises daily has been a lifesaver for me. After the ice bath and weight bearing, I am able to get some other exercises in before the muscle tone takes over again.

The following are some of the upper extremity home exercises I was assigned after my time at the Taub Clinic. When doing these exercises, the important thing to remember is to pace yourself. When completed slowly, it gives the left arm a better opportunity to reach full range of motion and complete the task well. The tasks are challenging, and it is important to remember that progress comes in tiny steps and it's not always immediate. But by sticking with it, you will see amazing things happen.

- Supination task: Holding a dowel in your left hand with your forearm on the table, rotate your forearm so that the dowel supinates. Then rotate back into pronation and repeat ten times.
- Practice opening containers: Now if you are anything like me, you are probably thinking, how the f**k am I going to open containers with my left hand when I can barely even control it? You are not. What I do is I practice holding a container in my left hand to stabilize so I can open the jar with my right (good) hand. I need to use my right hand to place my left hand on the container, and once it is in position I squeeze, unscrewing the lid with my right hand.
- Wipe the table/wall: With my right hand, I place a towel in my left hand and onto a table in front of me. Then I move my left hand in circles to wipe the table. Three circles is one rep. Ten reps clockwise and ten reps counterclockwise. Same exercise can be repeated with your hand wiping on a wall. *Wax on, wax off.*
- Open and close the refrigerator: This is a tough one, and initially when I practiced opening the fridge with my left hand, I found I needed to place my left hand around the door handle with the help of my right hand. This is fine. Once your left hand is successfully on the refrigerator door, open it and close it. Ten reps.
- The more you are able to use your affected arm and hand to help with the daily activities of life, the better. It's okay if you can't do it. The attempt is the important part. I will also use my left hand to try and open doors, closets, cabinets, and drawers.
- I even use my left hand to help zip my coat. I bought some zipper pulls from Amazon and attach them to my coat so that the zipper is longer and easier for me to grip with

my left hand. Pro tip: Once the zipper is in the socket and ready to be pulled up by your affected hand, use your good hand to grip the side of the jacket opposite the zipper and anchor it down while you pull the zipper up with your affected hand. *Boom.*

I know doing tasks in this way seems hard, but I kid you not, the more you work at it, the better and easier it will get. You are cultivating the habit of use, so failure is not an option. As long as you are making an effort, you are promoting positive brain change.[65]

A special thank you to all the therapists I have had who have contributed in major ways to my recovery: Alyssa, Joel, Todd, Daniella, Dave, Danna Kay, Mary, Farris, Arielle, Deborah, Lynne, Arlise, Tina, Kayla, and Adria. Thank you so, so, so much for your commitment to my recovery and for always going the extra mile to make sure I receive the best possible therapy experience. Thank you to all my doctors, Dr. Solomon, Dr. Klingmeyer, Dr. Jasey, Dr. Bapineedu, Dr. DeSouza, Dr. Lacotte, and everyone else who has contributed to my recovery in some way. Because of you, I am the person I am today: strong, motivated, and energized to succeed and make continuous progress in my recovery. I am so thankful for everyone who has supported me along this journey. I truly am the luckiest girl in the world.

65　(Danna Kay King and Mary Bowman, Taub Clinic Home exercise program for author, 2019).

ACKNOWLEDGMENTS

First off, thank you x1,000,000 to my brilliant professor and friend, Eric Koester. I am so beyond thankful for you and the New Degree Press team for pushing me to take the leap, write the book (two books!), and for being there to support me at every step in the process.

In writing this book I have been blessed with the incredible opportunity to connect with many fellow stroke survivors and thrivers. I am so honored to be a part of the stroke and brain injury community and would like to thank all my "stroke friends" who have shown me what it really means to be positive. Special thanks to my Brain Buddies: Adrian, Bridget, Courtney, Darren, Jamie, Kristin, Leah, Joe, Michelle, Mimi, and Zolly. You are all awesome. Thank you for always managing to brighten my day.

In particular, I would also like to say a special thanks to the following friends, family, survivors, and thrivers who have supported me during the period of preorder for this book. Thanks to all of you. I have not only achieved, but exceeded, my goals:

Alex Lau
Alexander Spevack
Andrew Abramson
Andrew McDonald
Andy Fabac
Angela Lau
Angela Schroeder
Ann Borowiec
Barbara Viola
Bella Gerard
Benjamin W Saunders
Beth DeCicco
Brian Paterson
Bridget Niebanck
Brooke Brazer Ferguson
Bryn Dragalin
Bryony Dansey
Cal Mullan
Cara Benevenia and
Family
Carlos J Sanzo
Caroline Burley
Caroline Doherty
Casey Knerr
Catherine Wachtell
Charlie Niebanck
Chris Rosowicz
Christine Butchko
Christopher Lee
Clay M Pearson
Connor Griggs-Demmin
Cynthia Vlad

Dana McDonald
Devika Sharma
Donna Greenwell
Donna Niebanck
Dorothy Niebanck
Elizabeth Borowiec
Emily Corn
Emily Mignogni
Eric Koester
Farris Fakhoury
Fran Borowiec
Francisca Johanek
Grace Conroy
Graham Berstler
Greg Nance
Gregg Jones
Heidi Wesely
Itay Arad
Jaclyn DiGregorio
Jade Beguelin
Jakeem Johnson
Janellen Duffy
Jennifer Soller
Jillian Nash
Jim Niebanck
Joani Crean
Joanne Erickson
Joe Borges
Julie Moran
Karen Mongrella
Karen Murie
Karen Rait

Kathleen Mumma
Kelly McAloon
Kevin Weaver
Kristina Woodman Hodgdon
Lanny McDonald
Laura Belias-Yurek
Laura Howe
Laura W Dillon
Leanna Namovic
Lena Elsborg
Lisa Hart
Lori Hricik
Lyndon Wong
Madeleine Thornburn
Mariam George
Marissa Prezzano
Mark Morales
Martha Gallo
Meaghan O'Neill
Megan Crean

Megan Wallace
Mike M Farrell
Nefretire Orgue
Pam Sullivan
Parker Pearson
Patti Taylor
Peggi Einhorn
Peter Carter
Prudence Pigott
Rebecca Dixon
Rocky Liu
Ruth Dekker
Sarah Medina
Scott Pomann
Sophia Spinelli
Suzanne Hamilton
Tawnie Romero-Golic
Theodore Wachtell
Tyler Byrd
Yuriy Boguslavsky
Zolliam Perez

Thanks to all the doctors, therapists, friends, family, and strangers who have helped my family during my recovery. Know that you are always in my prayers and there are no words for how grateful I am for your support.

Finally, thank you to my incredible parents and siblings for putting up with me and always helping me when I need it. I love you so much.

APPENDIX

———

Introduction

"Stroke Facts | Cdc.Gov". 2020. Cdc.Gov. https://www.cdc.gov/stroke/facts.htm.

"Stroke | Cdc.Gov". 2020. Cdc.Gov. https://www.cdc.gov/stroke/index.htm.

Chapter 5

"Left Side Neglect Following Stroke – There Is More to the Picture." 2020. *Neurorehabdirectory.Com*. https://www.neurorehabdirectory.com/left-side-neglect-following-stroke-picture/.

Chapter 7

Dr. Dorothy Klingmeyer, conversation with the author, 22 June 2019.

Chapter 9

"Louis Bolk Instituut – Positive Health." 2020. *Louisbolk.Org*. http://www.louisbolk.org/health-nutrition/integrative-medicine-3/new-concept-of-health.

"Frequently Asked Questions." 2020. *Who.Int.* https://www.who.int/about/who-we-are/frequently-asked-questions.

2020. *Louisbolk.Org.* http://www.louisbolk.org/downloads/3108.pdf.

Chapter 10

"People With Half Their Brain Removed Are Doing Surprisingly Well." 2020. *Futurism.* https://futurism.com/neoscope/people-half-brain-removed-doing-well).

Kliemann, Dorit, Ralph Adolphs, J. Michael Tyszka, Bruce Fischl, B.T. Thomas Yeo, Remya Nair, Julien Dubois, and Lynn K. Paul. 2019. "Intrinsic Functional Connectivity of the Brain in Adults With a Single Cerebral Hemisphere." *Cell Reports* 29 (8): 2398–2407.e4. doi:10.1016/j.celrep.2019.10.067.

Chapter 12

"World Stroke Day Featuring Dr. Jill Bolte Taylor and Claudia Mason." 2020. *Facebook Watch.* https://www.facebook.com/shareyourstrokeofgenius/videos/530693587717508/.

Chapter 13

Ella Sofia, phone conversation with author, 23 July 2019.

Chapter 14

Alonzo Mourning, conversation with author, 1 August 2019.

2020. *Theneuronerds.Com.* https://www.theneuronerds.com/episodes/ep-92.

Chapter 15

Alonzo Mourning, conversation with author, 1 August 2019.

Chapter 16

"UCLA Mindful Awareness Research Center, Los Angeles, CA." 2020. *Uclahealth.Org.* https://www.uclahealth.org/marc/default.cfm.

Chapter 17

Ben Vereen, conversation with author, 8 December 2019.

Chapter 18

Mary Bowman, conversation with author, 12 June 2019.

Dr. Edward Taub, conversation with author, 27 June 2019.

Chapter 24

Jeroen Mars, conversation with author, 24 August 2019.

Dr. Hugh Snyder, conversation with author, 22 June 2019.

Chapter 25

"Run the Mile You're on: Greg Nance." 2019. *CJBS Insight.* https://insight.jbs.cam.ac.uk/2019/run-the-mile-youre-on-greg-nance/.

Chapter 26

"What Is Spoon Theory?" 2020. *Healthline.* https://www.healthline.com/health/spoon-theory-chronic-illness-explained-like-never-before.

Chapter 27

Terry Sullivan, conversation with author, 23 July 2019.

Chapter 28

Tawnie Golic Cox, conversation with author, 29 September, 2019.

Chapter 30
Terry Sullivan, conversation with author, 23 July 2019.

Chapter 31
"Maddistrokeofluck." 2020. *Maddistrokeofluck.* https://maddistrokeofluck.com/.

Chapter 32
Bridget Chiovari, phone conversation with author, 28 July 2019.

Chapter 34
"Atomic Habits: An Easy & Proven Way to Build Good Habits & Break Bad Ones." 2020. *James Clear.* https://jamesclear.com/atomic-habits.

Chapter 36
Lena Elsborg, conversation with author, 18 January 2020.

Alonzo Mourning, conversation with author, 1 August 2019.

Strategies
Danna Kay King and Mary Bowman, Taub Clinic Home exercise program for author, 2019.

Made in the USA
Monee, IL
13 November 2022

17690992R00125